To Barbara

Wedding A

With

G000058665

Bet you can't find a better
bargain in here!

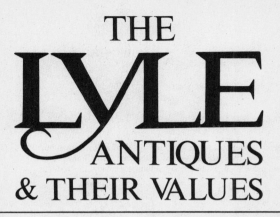

THE
LYLE
ANTIQUES
& THEIR VALUES

FURNITURE

Identification & Price Guide

COMPILED & EDITED BY
TONY CURTIS

The publishers wish to express their sincere thanks to the following for their involvement and assistance in the production of this volume:—

KAREN DOUGLASS
JANICE MONCRIEFF
ANNETTE CURTIS
TANYA FAIRBAIRN
SALLY DALGLIESH
DOUGLAS SAYERS
FRANK BURRELL
ROBERT NISBET
LOUISE SIMPSON
JONN DUNLOP
EILEEN BURRELL
SARAH RITCHIE

Printed in Denmark by ⊕ Nørhaven A/S, Viborg
ISBN 0-86248-103-1

INTRODUCTION

While this series of handy volumes has been specially devised to provide busy dealers and collectors with an extremely comprehensive reference library of antiques and their values, the information will also prove to be of great general interest to those with just a few pieces they wish to sell or appraise.

Each volume is crammed with over 2,000 detailed illustrations highlighting the distinguishing features of a broadly representative selection of specialised antiques and collectibles accompanied by descriptions and prices computed from recent auction figures.

We have endeavoured to obtain a balance between the more expensive collector's items and those which, although not in their true sense antiques, are handled daily by the antiques trade.

The illustrations and prices in the following sections have been arranged to make it easy for the reader to assess the period and value of all items with speed.

When dealing with the more popular trade pieces, in some instances a calculation of an average price has been estimated from the varying accounts researched.

As regards prices, when 'one of a pair' is given in the description the price quoted is for a pair and so that we can make maximum use of the available space it is generally considered that one illustration is sufficient. This will also apply when a description reads eg; part of a service, suite or a set.

It will be noted that in some descriptions taken directly from sales catalogues originating from many different countries, some terms are used in a broader sense than is customary, but in all cases the term used is self explanatory.

Pocket size with a sturdy binding, perfect for use in shops, flea markets and at auctions, *The Lyle Antiques and Their Values Identification and Price Guides* are your keys to smart antique buying or selling.

Tony Curtis

ACKNOWLEDGEMENTS

Abridge Auctions, (Michael Yewman) Market Place, Abridge, Essex RM4 1UA
Anderson & Garland, Anderson House, Market Street, Newcastle. NE1 6XA
Banks & Silvers, 66 Foregate Street, Worcester.
Barbers Fine Art Auctioneers, The Mayford Centre, Smarts Heath Road, Mayford, Woking.
Bearnes, Rainbow, Avenue Road, Torquay. TQ2 5TG
Biddle & Webb, Ladywood, Middleway, Birmingham. B16 0PP
Bloomsbury Book Auctions, 3 & 4 Hardwick Street, London.
Boardman Fine Art Auctioneers, Station Road Corner, Haverhill, Suffolk. CB9 0EY
Bonhams, Montpelier Galleries, Montpelier Street, Knightbridge, London. SW7 1HH
Bracketts, 27-29 High Street, Tunbridge Wells, Kent. TN1 1UU
J. R. Bridgford & Sons, 1 Heyes Lane, Alderley Edge, Cheshire.
British Antique Exporters, 206 London Road, Burgess Hill, W. Sussex. RH15 9RX
Brogden & Co., 38 & 39 Silver Street, Lincoln.
Wm. H. Brown, Westgate Hall, Grantham, Lincs. NG31 6LT
Lawrence Butler & Co., Butler House, 86 High Street, Hythe, Kent. CT21 5AJ
Capes, Dunn & Co., The Auction Galleries, 38 Charles Street, Manchester. M1 7DB
Chancellors Hollingsworth, 31 High Street, Ascot, Berkshire. SL5 7HG
Christie's, 8 King Street, St. James's, London. SW1Y 6QT
Christie's, 502 Park Avenue, New York, N. Y. 10022
Christie's, Cornelis Schuystraat 57, 1071 JG, Amsterdam, Holland.
Christie's East, 219 East 67th Street, New York, N. Y. 10021
Christie's & Edminston's, 164-166 Bath Street, Glasgow.
Christie's S. Kensington Ltd., 85 Old Brompton Road, London. SW7 3LD
Coles, Knapp & Kennedy, Georgian Rooms, Ross-on-Wye, Herefordshire. HR9 5HL
Cooper Hirst, Goldway House, Parkway, Chelmsford. CM20 7PR
Dacre, Son & Hartley, 1-5 The Grove, Ilkley, Yorkshire.
Dee & Atkinson, The Exchange Saleroom, Driffield, N. Humberside. YO25 7LJ
Dickson, Davy & Markham, Elwes Street, Brigg, S. Humberside. DN20 8LB
Wm. Doyle Galleries Inc., 175 East 87th Street, New York.
Dreweatts, Donnington Priory, Donnington, Newbury, Berkshire.
Hy. Duke & Son, Fine Art Salerooms, Weymouth Avenue, Dorchester, Dorset. DT1 1DG
Elliott & Green, Auction Salerooms, Emsworth Road, Lymington, Hants. SO4 9ZE
R. H. Ellis & Sons, 44-46 High Street, Worthing, West Sussex. BN11 1LL
Farrant & Wightman, 2/3 Newport Street, Old Town, Swindon.
John D. Fleming & Co., 8 Fore Street, Dulverton, Somerset. TA22 9EX
Fox & Sons, 5 & 7 Salisbury Street, Fordinbridge, Hants. SP6 1AD
Geering & Colyer, 22-26 High Street, Tunbridge Wells. TN1 1XA
Rowland Gorringe, 15 North Street, Lewes, Sussex.
Goss & Crested China Ltd., N. J. Pine, 62 Murray Road, Horndean, Hants. PO8 9JL
Andrew Grant, 59-60 Foregate Street, Worcester.
Graves, Son & Pilcher, 71 Church Road, East Sussex. BN3 2GL
Giles Haywood, The Auction House, St. John's Road, Stourbridge, W. Midlands. DY8 1EW
Heathcote Ball & Co., The Old Rectory, Appleby Magna, Leicestershire.
Hobbs & Chambers, 'At the Sign of the Bell', Market Place, Cirencester, Gloucestershire. GL7 1QQ
Honiton Galleries, High Street, Honiton, Devon.
Edgar Horn, 46-50 South Street, Eastbourne, Sussex. BN21 4XB
Jacobs & Hunt, Lavant Street, Petersfield, Hampshire. GU32 3EF
W. H. Lane & Son, 64 Morrab Road, Penzance, Cornwall. TR18 2QT
Lawrence Fine Art, South Street, Crewkerne, Somerset. TA18 8AB
James & Lister Lea, 11 Newhall Street, Birmingham.
Locke & England, 18 Guy Street, Leamington Spa, Warwickshire. CV32 4DG
Thomas Love & Son, South St. John Street, Perth, Scotland.
R. J. Lucibell, 7 Fontayne Avenue, Rainham, Essex.
Mallams, 24 St. Michael's Street, Oxford.
May, Whetter & Grose, Cornubia Hall, Par, Cornwall.
Moore, Allen & Innocent, 33 Castle Street, Cirencester, Gloucestershire. GL7 1QD
Morphets, 4-6 Albert Street, Harrogate, Yorkshire. HG1 1JL
Neales of Nottingham, 192 Mansfield Road, Nottingham. NG1 3HX
D. M. Nesbit & Co., 7 Clarendon Road, Southsea, Hants. PO5 2ED
Onslows Auctioneers, 14-16 Carroun Road, London. SW8 1JT
Osmond, Tricks, Regent Street Auction Rooms, Clifton, Bristol, Avon. BS8 4HG
Outhwaite & Litherland, Kingsway Galleries, Fontenoy Street, Liverpool. L3 2BE
Phillips, The Old House, Station Road, Knowle, Solihull, W. Midlands. B93 0HT
Phillips Auctioneers, The Auction Rooms, 1 Old King Street, Bath, Avon. BA1 1DD
John H. Raby & Son, 21 St. Mary's Road, Bradford.
Reeds Rains, Trinity House, 114 Northenden Road, Sale, Manchester. M33 3HD
Russell, Baldwin & Bright, Ryelands Road, Leominster, Herefordshire. HR6 8JG
Sandoe, Luce Panes, Wotton Auction, Rooms, Wotton-under-Edge, Gloucestershire. GL12 7EB
Robert W. Skinner Inc., Bolton Gallery, Route 117, Bolton, Massachusetts.
H. Spencer & Sons Ltd., 20 The Square, Retford, Notts.
Stalker & Boos, 280 North Woodward Avenue, Birmingham, Michigan.
David Stanley Auctions, Stordan Grange, Osgathorpe, Leics. LE12 9SR
Street Jewellery Society, 10 Summerhill Terrace, Newcastle-upon-Tyne.
Stride & Son, Southdown House, St. John's Street, Chichester, Sussex.
G. E. Sworder & Sons, Chequers, 19 North Street, Bishops Stortford, Herts.
Theriault, P. O. Box 151 Annapolis, Maryland 21404.
Vidler & Co., Auction Offices, Cinque Ports At., Rye, Sussex.
Wallis & Wallis, West Street Auction Galleries, Lewes, Sussex. BN7 2NJ
Ward & Partners, 16 High Street, Hythe, Kent.
Warner, Wm. H, Brown, 16-18 Halford Street, Leicester. LE1 1JB
Warren & Wignall, 113 Towngate, Leyland, Lancashire.
Peter Wilson Fine Art Auctioneers, Victoria Gallery, Market Street, Nantwich. CW5 3DG
Wooley & Wallis, The Castle Auction Mart, Castle Street, Salisbury, Wiltshire. SP1 3SU
Eldon E. Worrall & Co., 15 Seel Street, Liverpool.
Worsfolds Auction Galleries, 40 Station Road West, Canterbury, Kent.

CONTENTS

PERIODS

TUDOR PERIOD	1485 - 1603
ELIZABETHAN PERIOD	1558 - 1603
INIGO JONES	1572 - 1652
JACOBEAN PERIOD	1603 - 1688
STUART PERIOD	1603 - 1714
A. C. BOULLE	1642 - 1732
LOUIS XIV PERIOD	1643 - 1715
GRINLING GIBBONS	1648 - 1726
CROMWELLIAN PERIOD	1649 - 1660
CAROLEAN PERIOD	1660 - 1685
WILLIAM KENT	1684 - 1748
WILLIAM & MARY PERIOD	1689 - 1702
QUEEN ANNE PERIOD	1702 - 1714
GEORGIAN PERIOD	1714 - 1820
T. CHIPPENDALE	1715 - 1762
LOUIS XV PERIOD	1723 - 1774
A. HEPPLEWHITE	1727 - 1788
ADAM PERIOD	1728 - 1792
ANGELICA KAUFMANN	1741 - 1807
T. SHERATON	1751 - 1806
LOUIS XVI	1774 - 1793
T. SHEARER	(circa) 1780
REGENCY PERIOD	1800 - 1830
EMPIRE PERIOD	1804 - 1815
VICTORIAN PERIOD	1837 - 1901
EDWARDIAN PERIOD	1901 - 1910

MONARCHS

HENRY IV	1399 - 1413
HENRY V	1413 - 1422
HENRY VI	1422 - 1461
EDWARD IV	1461 - 1483
EDWARD V	1483 - 1483
RICHARD III	1483 - 1485
HENRY VII	1485 - 1509
HENRY VIII	1509 - 1547
EDWARD VI	1547 - 1553
MARY	1553 - 1558
ELIZABETH	1558 - 1603
JAMES I	1603 - 1625
CHARLES I	1625 - 1649
COMMONWEALTH	1649 - 1660
CHARLES II	1660 - 1685
JAMES II	1685 - 1689
WILLIAM & MARY	1689 - 1695
WILLIAM III	1695 - 1702
ANNE	1702 - 1714
GEORGE I	1714 - 1727
GEORGE II	1727 - 1760
GEORGE III	1760 - 1820
GEORGE IV	1820 - 1830
WILLIAM IV	1830 - 1837
VICTORIA	1837 - 1901
EDWARD VII	1901 - 1910

6

FURNITURE

F ine furniture is undoubtedly one of the best investments that can be made today because there is a limited supply of it around and prices for good quality pieces rise steadily, ignoring the peaks and troughs of other types of financial speculations.

No one who paid £1,000 for a George II table in the 1970's will be regretting their outlay today because it could bring back as much as £13,000 which was the sum paid for a George II satinwood sofa table at Phillips in London.

Edwardian satinwood and inlaid Carlton House desk by Druce & Co., 53in. wide.
£5,800

of a Carlton House desk made £8,000 which was what genuine Carlton House pieces were selling for only a short time ago and a Victorian partners' desk, copied from a Georgian original, made £19,000 at Phillips.

While reproduction sets of chairs are now selling well into the £2,000 – £3,000 range, sets like twelve William IV dining chairs found a buyer at £12,800 in London. A set of another dozen Regency carved mahogany chairs with sabre legs also made the high price of £22,000 when sold recently.

A William and Mary burr walnut bureau, the fall-flap enclosing a fitted interior with a well, 41in. wide. (Christie's)   £9,720

The furniture price inflation concentrates on quality and covers many periods and parts of the world – a mahogany and maple square sofa made in New England around 1805 sold recently for $46,000; a George III mahogany desk, that was reputed to have belonged to Dr Johnson, went for £40,000 in London; a Regency mahogany and ormolu library table fetched £12,000 and a Louis XV kingwood floral marquetry bombe commode, stamped by Nicholas Petit, made £13,500 at Phillips' London auction rooms.

Even copies of older pieces of furniture hit the high spots, providing they were of good quality. For example a Victorian copy

One of a set of twelve mahogany dining chairs, including a pair of armchairs, of George III style. (Christie's)   £21,600

FURNITURE

A Queen Anne scarlet lacquer bureau cabinet, decorated overall in raised gilt with chinoiserie figures and birds, 37½in. wide. (Christie's) £32,400

An Italian ebony and pietra dura cabinet-on-stand with three-quarter balustraded gallery, 47in. wide. (Christie's) £18,700

A Japanese lacquer cabinet on William and Mary stand with chased gilt metal clasps, 37in. wide. (Lawrence Fine Art) £27,500

Decorated furniture has always had a strong appeal and a Queen Anne green and gold lacquer cabinet, that was sold by Christie's, made £77,000 while an early Victorian ormolu and pietra dura cabinet sold for £4,620. There is also a rising market for Japanese lacquered pieces of furniture ranging from small boxes to bigger pieces and a 17th century ebonised and lacquer side cabinet with a red marble top made £16,500 while a more recent 19th century black lacquered cabinet on a stand fetched just over £1,500.

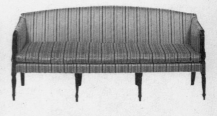

A Federal upholstered mahogany sofa on turned reeded legs with birch inlay, Mass., 1790-1810, 79in. wide. (Christie's) £7,897

Watch out for a rise in the price of lacquered screens. An 18th century Chinese coromandel twelve leaf screen with each leaf 19 inches wide and 93.5 inches high, has just made £41,800 and a Regency black and gold lacquer six leaf screen fetched £6,820. These are prized by decorators and collectors for their decorative value and there is also a strong market for screens of all sorts including painted leather which can make around £1,500 for a four leaf screen and more recent ones like the ebonised and marquetry Art Deco example which made £1,540 at Christie's this year.

One of the most significant developments in the furniture world in recent years is the rising interest in items from the last hundred years. The buying fraternity is

A three-sectioned oak screen, by Gustav Stickley, circa 1913, each panel 21½in. wide, 66in. high. (Robt. W. Skinner Inc.) £5,000

now split into 'old pieces' people and those who avidly seek out new trends, of which there are many.

Furniture styles since 1870 fall into five distinctive periods beginning with the Aesthetic Movement which ran from about 1870 to 1900 and which is characterised by pieces of furniture in the 'mediaeval' style or richly decorated with flowers like the dresser painted with water lilies which Phillips sold for £400. Another beautiful piece from this period that demanded the price of over £50,000 when it appeared for auction was a magnificent fruitwood marquetry cabinet designed by Emile Galle, better known for his work with glass.

An 18th century Chinese coromandel lacquer twelve-leaf screen, each leaf 19in. wide, 93½in. high. (Christie's)   £41,800

An English Arts & Crafts brass mounted mahogany, sycamore and walnut marquetry partner's desk, 129.6cm. wide. (Christie's) £2,484

An Arts & Crafts mahogany four-fold embroidered screen, 152cm. high. (Christie's) £825

The Aesthetic Movement was followed by the Arts and Crafts period, characterised particularly by the work of William Morris, which reached its peak of popularity around the turn of the century and lasted until about 1910. An example of this period is an Arts and Crafts movement painted cabinet and bookshelves, decorated with figures drawn by M. Reed, which was sold for £320 this year. The designer C. A. Voysey was also working at this time and his rush seated chairs in oak with cut out hearts on the back spar can now fetch over £16,500 for a pair.

FURNITURE

There is still a good deal of furniture around from the Arts and Crafts time because many large houses were refurbished and furnished by Morris's company. "Clouds" in Wiltshire is a case in point because the Hon. Percy Wyndham, owner of Clouds, commissioned Philip Webb and Morris Co. to design and refurbish his house between 1881 and 1889 and the contents began coming onto the auction market this year.

An Art Nouveau mahogany and inlaid dressing table with cartouche-shaped bevelled swing-frame mirror, 122cm. wide. (Phillips)
£520

The Arts and Crafts movement was supplanted by the Art Nouveau era which finished about 1925. The Art Nouveau period first saw the emergence of the designers of the Vienna School and, in this country, of Charles Rennie Mackintosh, who set the tone for much of the design of the period. German designers were extremely active through this period and their pieces which come up for sale have an extraordinarily modern look. A stained beechwood and aluminium writing table that Otto Wagner designed for the Oesterrichische Potsparkasse around 1906, fetched $46,750 when it was auctioned in New York this year.

One of a pair of Finimar laminated birchwood open armchairs designed by Alvar Alto. (Christie's)
£1,430

Finally, the 1930's saw the emergence of the Modernist style which lasted until after World War Two when the truly Modern Period began.

This last period has been dominated by Italian, Scandinavian and American designers. It also seems that post war designers have made distinct advances in the design of chairs and some of the examples now appearing in salerooms will certainly become the museum pieces of the future — for example, a blue PVC inflatable armchair sold by Christie's recently for £378 and a pair of black leather and steel Barcelona chairs by Mies van der Rohe which Christie's also sold for £770.

A blue PVC inflatable armchair. (Christie's)
£378

FURNITURE

Perhaps the most desirable period of all among the present day collectors of modern furniture is the Art Nouveau period and one of the great names in design is, of course, the Scot Charles Rennie Mackintosh whose furniture is now fought over by multi-millionaires and museum curators when it appears for auction. White lacquered furniture by Mackintosh is the most desirable and a chair in this style can fetch as much as £20,000 but even less decorative pieces like a rather battered stained oak side chair that he designed for Miss Cranston's Ingram Street tearooms in Glasgow in 1909 can cost around £5,000. The Mackintosh mania has gone to such heights that a set of six electro-plated teaspoons designed by him for Miss Cranston's tearoom recently made £240 and one menu card for Miss Cranston's White Cockade tearooms, printed with a design by his wife Margaret Macdonald, fetched an astonishing £460.

A tub armchair by Rennie Mackintosh for the Ingram Street Tea Rooms in Glasgow. (Christie's) £3,000

restrained type of dresser in the English Art Nouveau style with a bevelled mirror back sold for £980.

There was a great upsurge of designing talent in Scotland, particularly in the Glasgow College of Art at the turn of the century and as well as the Mackintoshes, collectors today have reason to respect names like Dr Christopher Dresser and E. A. Taylor, husband of the artist Jessie Marion King. Both of these men were polymath designers, turning out silver and metal ware, jewellery and stained glass as well as furniture and their work has had a strong influence in successive designers.

A dark stained oak dining chair designed by Charles Rennie Mackintosh, 1897. £12,100

Mackintosh's popularity has also had a strong knock-on effect for the rest of the furniture market, inflating prices of pieces made by his contemporaries and imitators. For example an Art Nouveau mahogany display cabinet in 'the Scottish style' which would have been consigned to the junk yard a few years ago as being totally unfashionable, recently made £650 at Christie's in Glasgow. A slightly more

A Christopher Dresser ebonised bedside cabinet with brass drop loop handle, and fitted interior, 36.4cm. wide. £3,890

FURNITURE

This spread of talent shown by Dresser and Taylor was also evident in people like Hector Gruimard, designer of the Paris Metro stations, who made elegant furniture as well and Charles Voysey, an architect turned designer, whose chairs today sell for between £13,000 and £15,000 each.

An oak settle with slats and spring cushion seat, by Gustav Stickley, circa 1907, 79in. long. (Robt. W. Skinner Inc.) £5,590

A Liberty oak dressing table with adjustable mirror, 132.6cm. wide with flaps extended. (Christie's) £432

As well as paying high prices for chairs and cabinets, collectors are also showing a strong demand for dressing tables and dining room sets in the Art Nouveau style and Phillips recently sold a dressing table for over £500, while a slightly later Art Deco style dressing table made by Liberty's fetched £432. An Art Deco mahogany and sycamore cocktail cabinet by Epstein and Goldbart made £500 in a London sale this year and another Art Deco cocktail bar trolley with glass panels by Lalique, sold for £6,480. It was the glass that made the difference.

Art Deco furniture is particularly popular in France where special rare items can make many thousands of pounds and recently in London a bulky looking walnut veneered Art Deco dining room suite, not by any famous designer, made £520. Names to look for in modern furniture include Gustav Stickley, Ponti and Bugatti who produced pieces decorated with bone inlays and beaten copper.

Pair of side chairs by Carlo Bugatti. (Christie's) £6,800

Finally some attention should be paid by collectors to pianos which have started to make considerable prices. A Steinway grand piano built in 1914 and reconditioned by Steinway in the '30's, with a painted inner lid, made $28,000 in New York and a 1900 W. Menzel Secessionist piano in a mahogany case with brass mounts, also sold well. Gone are the days when people with unwanted pianos chopped them up for firewood.

A leather topped footstool, by Gustav Stickley, 20¼in. wide. (Robt. W. Skinner Inc.) £625

ARMOIRES

One of a pair of Louis XVI kingwood armoires with two pairs of cupboards filled with gilt wire, 70in. wide. £15,120

A 17th century Flemish rosewood and ebony armoire with massive bun feet, 91in. wide. £2,420

A 17th century South German walnut armoire, 79in. wide. £6,700

Fine Victorian mahogany and walnut armoire with two keys, 1865. £520

An 18th century German walnut veneered and marquetry armoire, 78in. wide. £10,840

An 18th century French provincial oak armoire fitted with two panelled doors, 52in. wide. £675

A French gold and parcel gilt armoire squat cabriole feet. £1,600

An 18th century Dutch walnut armoire, the bombe lower part fitted with three drawers, 1.83m. wide. £2,200

A Dutch hardwood armoire, possibly Colonial, 64in. wide. £700

ARMOIRES

A Louis XVI amaranth,
tulipwood and parquetry
armoire, possibly Dutch,
41in. wide.   £3,240

A 17th century Tuscan
walnut armoire, 6ft.7in.
high.   £6,160

A mid 18th century French
provincial cherrywood
armoire with moulded cor-
nice, 56in. wide.   £1,620

Victorian oak armoire in
Art Nouveau style, 1900.
         £170

A 17th century Dutch walnut
and ebony armoire, 76in.
wide.   £1,320

A Louis XV carved oak
armoire with foliate vase
and scroll motifs, 5ft.6in.
wide, circa 1770.   £1,485

A mid 18th century Breton
walnut armoire with a drawer
in the base, 4ft.10in. wide.
         £1,760

A South African stinkwood
armoire on claw and ball
feet, with silver handles
stamped IB, 64in. wide.
         £1,730

A Louis XV provincial oak
armoire with brass barrel
hinges and escutcheon plates,
60in. wide.   £880

ARMOIRES

An 18th century Scandin-
avian walnut armoire,
57in. wide.   £3,780

A Louis XV cherrywood
armoire with moulded
chamfered cornice, 56in. wide.
                       £4,180

A Dutch fruitwood armoire
with a pair of shaped panelled
doors, 76in. wide, 96in. high.
                       £4,400

Late 18th/early 19th cen-
tury oak armoire with
moulded cornice, 69½in.
wide.   £860

An 18th century French
provincial oak armoire, 6ft.
2in. wide.   £1,050

A classical mahogany
armoire, attributed to Chas.
H. Lannvier, circa 1800-15,
55in. wide.   £16,805

A French provincial fruitwood
armoire on squat cabriole legs,
61in. wide.   £1,650

An 18th century South
German figured and burr
walnut armoire, 74in. wide.
                       £14,300

Mid 18th century French
provincial oak armoire with
moulded foliate cornice,
64in. wide, 88in. high.
                       £4,180

BEDS

A George III mahogany four-post bedstead, 5ft.2in. wide, 6ft.9in. long, 7ft.6in. high.
£4,000

A late Federal carved cherry-wood four-post bedstead, probably New York, circa 1825, 53¼in. wide.   £3,990

A giltwood four-post bed with padded arched head-rest, box-spring and mattress, circa 1830, 64in. wide,
£7,150

An Empire mahogany lit en bateau with box spring, 54in. wide, 73in. long.   £3,240

Mahogany and inlaid bed, 4ft.6in. wide, circa 1900.
£150

Majorelle mahogany bed with semi-circular bed head, circa 1900, 201cm. wide.   £330

A Georgian mahogany four-post bed, the canopy with breakfront cornice on reeded posts inlaid with satinwood panels, 72in. wide.
£4,105

A mahogany four-post bed with box spring and mattress covered in pale green repp, 18th century and later, 82½in. long.   £7,150

A mahogany four-poster bed with box spring, 60in. wide.
£1,945

BEDS

A 17th century oak four-poster bed with panelled headboard, 64in. wide, 93in. high.   £2,700

A mahogany four-poster bed with moulded canopy and floral chintz hangings, George III and later, 60in. wide.   £2,915

A Regency parcel gilt and fruitwood four-post bed, 43½in. wide, 96in. high.   £3,850

Painted Empire maple masonic bed, N.Y., circa 1830, 54in. wide.   £420

A Gustav Stickley oak bed, designed by Harvey Ellis, 59½in. wide.   £16,670

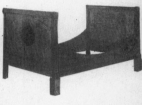

An Empire mahogany bed, the head and foot-end inlaid with brass musical trophies, 43¾in. wide.   £1,100

A mahogany four-post bed with waved shaped and moulded cornice, 94in. wide.   £1,510

A mahogany four-poster bed with plain headboard and square pillars, 61in. wide, 84in. high.   £1,945

An Elizabethan oak tester bed with box-spring mattress, 7ft. wide overall, circa 1580-1603.   £20,900

BEDS

A Victorian Gothic oak half tester bed, which lodged Prince Albert. £800

A 19th century French carved and gilded bed, circa 1860, 6ft. wide. £5,280

A Victorian papier-mache bed by H. Schmurmoff & Co., Birmingham. £4,400

A Regency mahogany and brass campaign bed, with inscribed brass plaque 'Butler's Patent, Catherine St.', 26in. wide. £3,960

Late 19th century Eastlake influence walnut bed, America, 58½in. wide. £430

A Federal maple highpost bedstead, New England, 1800-20, 54in. wide. £2,900

A late Federal figured maple bedstead, 62in. wide, overall. £1,300

A parcel gilt and cream-painted four-post bed, with padded headboard and yellow repp pleated hangings, box spring and mattress, 83.5in. wide. £1,080

Early 19th century Federal painted walnut pencil-post bedstead, North Carolina, 52½in. wide, overall. £2,900

BEDS

Late 19th century Victorian brass bed, America, 87in. wide. £1,620

Mid 19th century Louis XV style walnut bed with scrolled and moulded headboard, 5ft.6in. wide, made in France. £460

A Federal mahogany high-post bedstead, Mass., 1790-1810, with D-shaped head-board, 53½in. wide. £2,785

A 17th century oak four-poster bed, the tester with moulded cornice and carved frieze, 156cm. wide. £2,200

A Federal maple and birch tall post tester bed, New England, circa 1820, 57in. wide, 80in. long. £2,465

A mahogany four-post bed with box-spring and mattress, 59in. wide. £1,650

A rococo Revival walnut bed, America, circa 1860, 91in. high, 74in. long. £1,740

One of a pair of Arts & Crafts inlaid beds, attri-buted to Herter Bros., circa 1870, oak burl and other veneers, 26½in. wide. £960

A Federal carved maple high-post bedstead, Mass., 1790-1810, 57in. wide. £4,965

FURNITURE

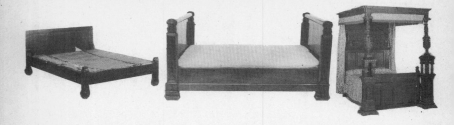

An oak bed with panelled headboard on square legs with rollers, late 16th century, 52in. wide.   £2,200

A mahogany lit en bateau, three-quarter size, circa 1830, 43½in. high.   £695

A North Country Charles II oak tester bedstead, circa 1670, 5ft.9in. wide, 7ft.7in. long.   £3,190

An Art Deco grand lit en lac d'or, 179cm. wide.   £900

Victorian brass and iron bed, 1875.   £200

A large sycamore bed, circa 1955, signed by Louis Sognot.   £2,470

A Charles I oak tester bedstead, circa 1640, 4ft.7½in. wide.   £8,250

Victorian mahogany bed head, circa 1880.   £200

Late 19th century Jacobean style oak bedstead.   £150

BEDS

A white-painted and gilt
four-poster bed with
George III arms on the
tester.   £16,000

A Portuguese rosewood bed
with pierced open headboard
and with box spring, 18th
century, 42in. wide. £2,050

American Victorian maple
and bird's-eye maple veneer
bamboo crib, circa 1870,
53½in. long.   £250

A 19th century oak four-
poster bed, the head and
foot inset with earlier
panels in coloured woods,
145cm. wide.   £3,600

An Empire mahogany lit en
bateau with box spring
mattress, 48in. wide, 86in.
long.   £3,300

A late Federal carved mahogany bedstead, the footposts
on brass ball feet, 57in. wide.
          £6,110

Federal tiger maple tall post
bed, New England, circa
1830, 54in. wide, 72in. long.
          £1,230

A Federal carved mahogany
four-post bedstead, Mass.,
circa 1820, 76in. long, 47¼in.
wide.   £4,355

A Renaissance Revival walnut
and burl veneer bed and chest,
bearing the label 'E. D. Trymby's,
Phila., Penn.'.   £2,250

BONHEUR DU JOUR

A 19th century French ebonised and boulle bonheur du jour with pull-out writing slide, 30in. wide. £1,100

A mahogany and satinwood crossbanded bonheur du jour by T. Willson, London, 45in. wide. £760

A 19th century French rosewood and marquetry bonheur du jour. £950

A George III mahogany and satinwood bonheur du jour with leather lined writing slide, 26¼in. wide. £1,620

A George III burr-yew and satinwood bonheur du jour with a recessed central cupboard door, 35½in. wide. £4,105

A George III tulipwood-veneered bonheur du jour, on square tapering legs, circa 1790, 2ft.6in. wide. £5,060

A lady's inlaid walnut writing desk, the superstructure with a pair of glazed cupboards, 2ft. 10½in. wide. £1,280

A George III mahogany bonheur du jour, the superstructure with two oval-inlaid doors, 36¼in. wide. £3,780

An ormolu mounted kingwood bonheur du jour, the superstructure with inset mottled grey marble top, 28¾in. wide. £1,835

BONHEUR DU JOUR

French satinwood parquetry decorated bonheur du jour with inset clock by Leroy.　　　£1,100

Mid Victorian lady's mahogany writing desk on French cabriole supports, 47½in. wide.　　　£800

A French rosewood and ormolu mounted bonheur du jour, circa 1890, 3ft. 3in. wide.　　　£750

A 19th century French bonheur du jour, the ebonised ground decorated with panels of foliate scrolls, 38in. wide.　　　£1,540

A Louis XVI-style bonheur du jour, veneered in exotic woods, 31in. long. £1,700

A mahogany bonheur du jour surmounted by pierced brass gallery, circa 1780, 3ft.5in. wide.　　　£715

A 19th century amboyna table in French style by W. Williamson & Sons, 31in. wide.　　　£1,900

A Victorian serpentine fronted walnut and kingwood crossbanded bonheur du jour in the French style, circa 1860, 4ft.5in. wide. £1,600

A Regency period rosewood veneered gilt and brass inlaid bonheur du jour in the manner of John McLean, 26½in. wide.　　　£4,600

BOOKCASES

A George III carved mahogany bookcase on stand with scroll carved hairy paw feet, 1.56m. wide. £2,400

A George IV mahogany breakfront bookcase, inlaid with brass medallions, 8ft.4in. wide, circa 1825. £3,740

A late Federal tiger maple bookcase, in two parts, possibly New York, 1810-20, 52½in. wide. £4,715

A Regency mahogany open bookcase on turned feet, 34½in. wide. £1,730

A mahogany breakfront bookcase with moulded broken pediment, 80in. wide. £2,915

One of a pair of Regency mahogany and crossbanded open bookcases, 2ft.7½in. wide, circa 1810. £1,100

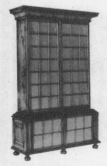

An oak book press of the Pepys model with glazed cupboard doors on bun feet. £4,105

A late Federal mahogany breakfront bookcase, Phila., 1815-20, 108in. wide. £18,870

A George II mahogany bookcase, the doors opening to a divided interior, circa 1730-50, 58¼in. wide. £5,345

BOOKCASES

A late Victorian mahogany breakfront bookcase, the bookshelves enclosed by glazed tracery doors, 8ft. 2in. wide.　£4,000

A George III mahogany bookcase, banded with satinwood, 53in. wide.　£19,800

A Regency burr yew breakfront bookcase supplied by Marsh & Tatham to the Prince of Wales at Carlton House, 73½in. wide.　£145,800

A Regency rosewood dwarf bookcase, formerly with a superstructure, 42¼in. wide.　£5,400

A William IV mahogany standing open bookcase, 33in. wide.　£1,300

A George IV rosewood dwarf bookcase with adjustable open shelves, 44in. wide.　£880

A mid Georgian mahogany bookcase with pair of glazed doors with egg-and-dart carved astragals, 73½in. wide.　£8,250

A Regency mahogany breakfront bookcase in the manner of Gillows, with six glazed doors, 143½in. wide.　£25,920

A Regency mahogany bookcase in the Gothic style, 29in. wide.　£5,500

BOOKCASES

A Victorian carved mahogany library bookcase on plinth base, 2ft.10in. wide.
£340

Gustav Stickley two-door bookcase, circa 1910, no. 716, gallery above eight-pane doors, 42in. wide.
£1,330

A George III satinwood bookcase on later turned feet, circa 1790, 2ft.4in. wide.
£4,180

A Regency mahogany dwarf bookcase with four graduated shelves above a drawer, 30in. wide.
£1,980

A Regency mahogany breakfront bookcase with raspberry moire silk lined interior, 108in. wide.
£17,600

Six section Globe Wernicke cabinet, 1880.
£290

A George III mahogany breakfront bookcase with a pair of glazed cupboard doors, 97½in. wide.
£5,400

A George II mahogany and crossbanded mahogany cabinet bookcase, circa 1740, 3ft.9in. wide.
£2,200

A Victorian oak breakfront library bookcase, the top section enclosed by four glazed panel doors, 88in. wide.
£1,500

BOOKCASES

Kingwood banded satin-
wood revolving book
shelves.   £320

A Regency rosewood dwarf
bookcase, the breakfront
with grey marble top, 83in.
wide.   £11,880

An early 19th century
Regency brass inlaid ebony
open bookcase, 54in. wide.
£9,180

Gustav Stickley leaded single
door bookcase, designed by
Harvey Ellis, circa 1904, no.
700, 36in. wide.   £5,245

A Regency purpleheart
pedestal bookcase with
square 17th century Italian
marble top formed in two
segments, 23in. sq. £22,000

Large stripped pine bookcase
on cupboard, the two glazed
doors enclosing three shaped
shelves, 7ft. high.   £600

A large Regency mahogany
breakfront bookcase, the
base with six panelled cupboard doors, 176in. wide.
£4,180

A Charles II oak bookcase
with a pair of glazed and
panelled cupboard doors,
55in. wide.   £7,560

An early Victorian oak breakfront bookcase, by A. W. N.
Pugin and John Webb, now
painted white, 146in. wide.
£4,950

BUREAU BOOKCASES

A Dutch marquetry and mahogany bureau bookcase in three sections, circa 1760, 3ft.9in. wide.   £9,460

A Chinese padoukwood bureau cabinet, the pair of doors each with a mirrored glass painting, circa 1780, 3ft.8in. wide.   £31,900

A Chippendale block front desk and bookcase in two sections, Mass., 1760-80, 40½in. wide.   £25,130

A George II mahogany bureau cabinet, the fall front enclosing a fitted interior with drawers, 1.04m. wide.   £5,000

A George II mahogany bureau cabinet with original brass ring handles, 42in. wide.   £3,600

An 18th century Anglo-Dutch kingwood, burr yewwood and amboyna oyster veneered bureau cabinet, 1.98m. high.   £2,900

A Chippendale mahogany blockfront secretary desk, circa 1780, 42in. wide.   £34,720

A George I walnut bureau cabinet with later-glazed arched cupboard door, 21½in. wide.   £17,280

A Queen Anne walnut bureau bookcase with candle slides, 41½in. wide.   £10,450

BUREAU BOOKCASES

A Queen Anne walnut bureau cabinet with two candle slides, 39in. wide. **£5,400**

Early 20th century Jacobean-style oak secretary, 30½in. wide. **£515**

An early George III mahogany bureau bookcase, the bureau with fitted interior, 40in. wide. **£2,860**

A George II oak bureau bookcase, the fall-front with concealed well, drawers, pigeon holes and central cupboard, 39in. wide. **£1,450**

A Queen Anne brown and gold lacquer bureau cabinet, the mirror cupboard doors enclosing a fitted interior, 40½in. wide. **£38,880**

A walnut bureau cabinet with a pair of mirror glazed doors, 32½in. wide. **£4,950**

An Edwardian inlaid mahogany bureau bookcase, 3ft. wide. **£620**

A Scandinavian green painted and parcel gilt secretaire bookcase, basically late 18th century, 47in. wide. **£2,200**

Edwardian mahogany inlaid bureau bookcase, shell inlay on fall-front, 35in. wide. **£750**

BUREAU BOOKCASES

A walnut bureau cabinet on bun feet, 3ft.4½in. wide, circa 1700.   £5,720

A Queen Anne walnut bureau cabinet, the fall-flap enclosing a fitted interior, 43½in. wide.   £36,720

A George III mahogany bureau bookcase on ogee bracket feet, 44in. wide.   £2,485

A Victorian painted and decorated pine secretary bookcase, Heywood Bros., painting attributed to E. and T. Hill, circa 1860, 49in. wide.   £7,255

A black and gold lacquer bureau cabinet, the mirrored cupboard doors enclosing a fitted interior, 40½in. wide.   £19,440

A Queen Anne walnut bureau cabinet, the baize lined sloping flap enclosing a fitted interior, 43in. wide.   £9,720

A George III mahogany bureau bookcase, the sloping flap enclosing a fitted interior, 43½in. wide.   £3,080

A George II padoukwood bureau cabinet, the sloping flap enclosing ten drawers, 34in. wide.   £6,050

A Chippendale style faded mahogany bureau bookcase on ogee bracket feet, 4ft. wide.   £2,700

BUREAU BOOKCASES

A Chippendale transitional mahogany secretary, circa 1790, 46in. wide. £3,990

An early George III mahogany bureau cabinet with an arched mirror glazed cupboard door, 33in. wide. £6,480

A Queen Anne walnut bureau-bookcase with fall-front, circa 1710, 36in. wide. £6,400

A George III mahogany bureau bookcase with astragal glazed doors, 124cm. wide, circa 1770. £1,430

A late 18th/early 19th century Italian scarlet lacquer and gilt bureau cabinet, 89cm. wide. £7,000

A Chippendale cherrywood desk and bookcase, in two sections, 1760-90, 41½in. wide. £12,220

1930's oak bureau bookcase with glazed top. £120

Mid 18th century Italian scarlet and gold lacquer bureau cabinet on cabriole legs and hoof feet, 37in. wide. £2,200

A George I walnut desk and bookcase, circa 1720, 38in. wide. £2,900

BUREAUX

A George III mahogany bureau, circa 1800, the painting circa 1890, 3ft. wide. £825

A Louis XV-style kingwood bureau de dame, 2ft.2in. wide, circa 1890. £570

Small Edwardian mahogany veneered bureau with fall front, 31in. wide. £300

A Country Federal cherry slant lid desk, New England, circa 1800, 40½in. wide. £1,230

A William and Mary burr-yew bureau, the sloping flap enclosing a stepped fitted interior, 31½in. wide. £3,455

An early Georgian walnut bureau, the sloping flap enclosing a fitted interior, 38½in. wide. £3,455

A mahogany bureau, line inlaid and crossbanded in rosewood with fall flap, 31½in. wide. £1,100

A Dutch walnut and floral marquetry bureau de dame of serpentine outline, 35in. wide. £2,420

A cylinder front desk with a raised superstructure of three drawers, 39in. wide. £1,210

BUREAUX

A Dutch walnut and marquetry bureau, the ogee sloping flap enclosing a fitted interior, 52in. wide. £4,320

Late 19th century lady's rosewood veneered cylinder bureau with inlaid marquetry sprays of flowers and stringing, 32in. wide. £800

An 18th century Italian walnut and bone inlaid bureau, the sloping flap enclosing a fitted interior, 50in. wide. £4,860

A George III mahogany and sycamore bureau with leather lined shaped spreading fall-flap enclosing a fitted interior, 30in. wide. £2,810

A Louis XV/XVI transitional period parquetry, marquetry and ormolu decorated bureau a cylindre veneered in tulipwood, kingwood and purpleheart, 1.44m. wide. £7,500

A George III mahogany bureau with leather lined sloping flap, 31½in. wide. £1,240

A William and Mary walnut bureau, the sloping flap enclosing a fitted interior, 38in. wide. £2,915

A mid 18th century German ormolu mounted black lacquered bureau cabinet, 53in. wide. £8,100

Mid 18th century Dutch Colonial padoukwood bureau with fitted interior, 41½in. wide. £3,890

33

BUREAUX

Mid 18th century German rococo miniature walnut veneer slant-front bureau, 18¼in. wide.   £1,150

An oak drop-front desk, by Gustav Stickley, circa 1912, 32in. wide.   £750

A Chippendale walnut slant top desk on claw and ball feet, probably Penn., circa 1780.   £6,990

A George II walnut knee-hole bureau of pale colour with chevron bandings throughout, 35in. wide.   £2,860

Late 18th century Italian satinwood and marquetry bureau, 50in. wide. £6,600

A cedar wood and walnut bureau, the sloping flap enclosing a fitted interior, the sides with carrying handles, 22½in. wide.
£755

Mid 18th century Chinese Export padoukwood bureau with four serpentine drawers, the back inscribed TH52, 39¾in. wide.   £12,100

Early 20th century oak bureau.   £205

A George III padoukwood bureau with moulded sloping lid enclosing a fitted interior, 31in. wide.   £2,375

BUREAUX

Gustav Stickley drop-front desk with cabinet doors, circa 1902-04, 32¾in. wide. £2,585

A Tuscan walnut bureau, constructed from a 16th century cupboard, 3ft.3in. wide. £715

A George I walnut bureau, the quarter baize lined flap inlaid with chevron banding enclosing a fitted interior, 29¼in. wide. £9,900

A Chippendale maple and pine slant front desk, New England, circa 1780, 39in. wide. £1,440

An Edwardian inlaid mahogany cylinder bureau with decorated urn front, 30in. wide. £525

Late 18th century George III mahogany slant-top desk with fitted interior, 39in. wide. £3,230

An early 18th century small walnut bureau. £4,100

Chippendale tiger maple desk, Rhode Island, circa 1770, exterior with original worn red paint, 36in. wide. £25,175

A Queen Anne walnut bureau with fall-front and stepped fitted interior, 28¾in. wide. £7,000

BUREAUX

Late 18th century Scandinavian maple and rosewood bureau, 43in. wide.   £865

An 18th century Continental walnut serpentine front bureau, 4ft.4in. wide.   £3,500

A Chippendale mahogany slant front desk, Mass., 1770-90.   £1,765

Chippendale tiger maple slant top desk with fall-front, New England, circa 1780, 42in. wide.   £5,770

A Country Federal cherry-wood slant front desk, Mass., circa 1800, 40½in. wide.   £1,095

An early Georgian walnut bureau, the leather lined sloping flap enclosing a fitted interior, 37in. wide.   £5,185

A George III mahogany bureau, the baize lined fall-flap flanked by two hinged flaps enclosing a fitted interior, 57½in. wide.   £14,580

Mid 18th century German rococo walnut veneered secretary, 38½in. wide.   £1,725

A Chippendale walnut slant-front desk with fitted interior, Rhode Island, 1760-90, 40¼in. wide.   £2,540

BUREAUX

Late 18th century George III painted satinwood bureau, re-veneered and painted in the 19th century, 2ft.8in. wide. **£3,190**

A walnut and other woods marquetry desk, Holland, circa 1760, 54in. wide. **£7,040**

An oak bureau with fall-front enclosing a fitted interior, 35in. long. **£550**

A Louis XV kingwood and marquetry bureau de dame by A. M. Criaerd, 29½in. wide. **£2,590**

A George III satinwood cylinder bureau, the top with leather lined domed tambour shutter, 30½in. wide. **£8,640**

A Chippendale tiger maple and maple slant top desk, New England, circa 1780, 36in. wide. **£1,875**

An early 18th century burr elm bureau in two parts with fall-front, 30½in. wide. **£3,500**

William and Mary pine fall-front desk, Mass., circa 1730, 36¼in. wide. **£9,230**

A German walnut and cross-banded bureau, the fall-front revealing a stepped and fitted interior, 3ft.3½in. wide, circa 1710. **£2,660**

A George IV mahogany cabinet, circa 1825, 3ft.5½in. wide.   £1,320

A Regency mahogany folio cabinet, the top with twin leather lined easels with further easel beneath, 42in. wide.   £3,455

An 18th century Portuguese Colonial rosewood table cabinet, the front with various sized drawers, 13in. wide.   £540

An Art Deco wrought iron and zebra wood cabinet, carved signature J. Cayette, Nancy, circa 1925, 115cm. high.   £1,405

An 18th century Indo-Portuguese cabinet on stand in nadum wood, 35in. wide.   £935

A Regency ebonised and lacquer dwarf cabinet with Carrara marble top and cedar lined interior, 39½in. wide.   £7,560

Mid 18th century mahogany side cabinet with Verde Antico marble top, 36½in. wide.   £1,375

One of a pair of Biedermeier satin birch and ebonised side cabinets, 21in. wide.   £1,295

A Regency pollard oak and burr-yew dwarf cabinet, the top with ebony bandings, 26in. wide.   £3,455

CABINETS

An ormolu mounted mahogany cabinet, the base with a pair of shibayama lacquer panel doors, 48¼in. wide.
£4,950

An Art Deco cocktail bar trolley, the bar handle flanked by two inset clear and satin glass panels by Lalique, 88cm. wide.
£6,480

A George III mahogany music cabinet with adjustable top, opening to reveal four sloping flaps, 26in. wide.
£3,190

Late 17th century Portuguese rosewood sewing cabinet carved with ripple mouldings, 21½in. wide.
£2,200

A William III walnut veneered cabinet on stand, the moulded frieze fitted with two drawers.
£2,700

A Sue et Mare rosewood, ebonised and marquetry music cabinet on elongated ebonised legs, 95.2cm. wide.
£3,025

An Ernest Gimson cedar wood cabinet, the interior fitted with sliding shelves, 116cm. high.
£770

One of a pair of rosewood dwarf cabinets with specimen marble tops, 29½in. wide.
£5,500

A lacquered stacking double cabinet on stand, each pair of doors and the sides painted in polychrome on gilt, 2ft.9in. wide.
£900

CABINETS

A 17th century ormolu mounted ebonised and Japanese lacquer side cabinet with red marble top, 52in. wide. £16,500

A 1930's cocktail cabinet with curved doors, 91cm. wide. £460

An 18th century vizigatapam ivory inlaid hardwood table cabinet, with carrying handles, 17½in. wide. £2,375

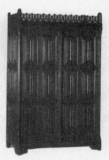

A Victorian inlaid walnut and gilt metal mounted side cabinet, 32in. wide. £440

A Chinese black and gold lacquer cabinet on Charles II silvered wood stand, the cabinet 17th century, 40in. wide. £15,120

An early Victorian oak cabinet, by A. W. N. Pugin and John Webb, 52in. wide. £2,640

A Regency lacquer side cabinet, the ebonised top with pierced ormolu gallery, 43¼in. wide. £8,640

A North German parcel gilt and walnut cabinet on chest, circa 1730, 45in. wide. £6,480

Late 19th century Regency-style mahogany demi-lune cabinet, 34in. wide. £450

CABINETS

A Regency brass inlaid ebony and satinwood breakfront side cabinet, 36½in. wide. £1,835

An early Victorian ormolu mounted ebony and pietra dura side cabinet, 43in. wide. £4,620

A North Italian walnut cabinet, with marquetry and ivory inlay, 4ft.9in. wide, circa 1700, with later additions. £750

A Brainerd & Armstrong Co. spool cabinet with twelve glass front drawers over one oak drawer, circa 1900, 37in. high. £370

Grain painted pine lawyer's cabinet, the panel doors opening to reveal thirty-eight compartments, New England, circa 1800, 33in. wide. £1,750

A Goanese ivory inlaid ebony and hardwood cabinet on stand, the drawers with ivory studs, 42in. wide. £10,260

A large varnished wook hikone mizuya kasandedansu, Meiji period, 170 x 193.3 x 50.1cm. £1,945

An oak bedside cabinet with bronze drop handles, by P. Waals assisted by P. Burchett, 1928, 78.9cm. high. £1,295

A Wm. Watt ebonised side cabinet designed by E. W. Godwin, 197.4cm. high by 128.6cm. wide. £5,400

41

CABINETS

Late 18th century Dutch mahogany inlaid dressing cabinet with hinged cover, 46½in. wide. £935

A late Victorian ebonised side cabinet in the Arts & Crafts style, 93cm. wide. £550

A George III mahogany dressing cabinet of D-shape outline, the hinged top in three sections, 50¾in. wide. £1,970

An Edwardian rosewood inlaid side cabinet, 54in. wide. £750

A William and Mary oyster veneered laburnum cabinet on stand, 37in. wide. £19,440

A decorated pine side cabinet designed and painted by H. Von Herkomer, 95cm. wide. £1,600

An early 20th century Louis XVI style ormolu mounted marble top music cabinet, 33½in. wide. £800

A Renaissance Revival inlaid rosewood cabinet, America, circa 1870, 36½in. wide. £1,320

French mahogany and kingwood ormolu mounted encoignure, circa 1860, 2ft.8in. wide. £640

CABINETS

An American mahogany
filing cabinet, 1880. £275

Art Deco cabinet of various
woods, 1930's.   £600

A Gustav Stickley oak music
cabinet, the ten pane single
door with amber glass, circa
1912, 47¼in. high.   £1,595

A George III mahogany collector's cabinet containing a
collection of shells, circa
1780, 2ft. wide.   £1,485

One of a pair of early George
III rosewood cabinets on
stands, each with pierced
fretwork gallery, 37in. wide.
                    £25,920

A 17th century Flemish
ebony, tortoiseshell and
painted cabinet on stand,
38in. wide.   £9,720

Regency satinwood and
ebony collector's cabinet,
the ebony handles with ivory
centres, 38in. wide. £12,100

An ebonised and ivory inlaid
side cabinet, the design attributed to T. E. Colcutt, 137cm.
wide.   £700

An Italian walnut cabinet
with a fall-front panel enclosing a fitted interior, the
carvings late 17th century,
27¾in. wide.   £1,320

CANDLESTANDS

FURNITURE

A Federal mahogany tilt-top candlestand, American, 1790-1810, 26½in. high.   £645

Chippendale cherry candlestand, probably Rhode Island, circa 1770, 25½in. high.   £525

A Federal mahogany candlestand with octagonal top, New England, 1790-1810, 21¼in. wide.   £380

Country Chippendale cherry octagonal top candlestand, probably Conn., circa 1760, 24.7/8in. high, 17¼in. diam.   £1,000

A Federal inlaid mahogany candlestand on a vase-turned pedestal, 1790-1810, 29½in. high.   £1,220

A Federal birch candlestand, original red stain finish, New England, circa 1790, 26¾in. high.   £1,330

A classical mahogany tilt-top candlestand, N.Y., circa 1820/40, 30¾in. high.   £680

A tripod cherry candlestand with candle drawer, Mass., circa 1760, 25½in. high.   £3,520

A Federal mahogany tilt-top candlestand, 1790-1810, 26in. wide.   £570

CANDLESTANDS

A Federal inlaid cherrywood candlestand, Connecticut River Valley, 1790-1810, 26¾in. high. £8,615

One of a pair of William and Mary marquetry candlestands, on later turned columns, 39in. high. £2,420

A maple black painted and decorated candlestand, New England, circa 1775-1800, 26in. high. £425

A Chippendale mahogany candlestand with tilt top, the legs terminating in padded snake feet, circa 1770, 27in. high. £2,220

A painted pine candlestand, New England, circa 1780, 27in. high, 20in. diam. £625

Chippendale mahogany candlestand, New England, circa 1780, 28½in. high. £695

A Chippendale mahogany bird cage candlestand, Phila., circa 1760, 27½in. high. £3,125

Chippendale cherry candlestand, the shaped top with ovolo corners, circa 1780, 26in. high. £1,750

A Federal maple candlestand, with circular dished top, New England, 1790-1810, 28½in. high, 17¼in. diam. £3,590

CANTERBURYS

A Regency mahogany canterbury, trade label of 'Andw. Fleming & Co., Kirkaldy', 20in. wide.   £2,160

The Herne's oak canterbury, dated 1863, 2ft. 4in. wide.   £1,100

A Regency rosewood canterbury on baluster legs, 20½in. wide.   £2,970

A George III satinwood canterbury, the hinged top with three-quarter gallery.   £8,250

A George IV mahogany and rosewood canterbury with gilt metal gallery, 51cm. wide, stamped Wilkinson.   £4,200

A Victorian walnut music canterbury on pierced lyre-shaped end supports, circa 1850, 2ft. wide.   £730

A Regency mahogany three-division canterbury with slatted sides and a drawer in the base, 19in. wide.   £650

A George III satinwood canterbury with four dipped slatted apertures above a drawer, circa 1790, 1ft.6in. wide.   £3,190

Late 18th century George III mahogany canterbury, 19½in. long, 21in. high.   £555

CANTERBURYS

A Victorian rosewood music canterbury with two drawers on turned feet, 19in. wide. £400

Regency rosewood canterbury with rectangular top and pierced undulating splayed gallery, 27½in. wide. £1,760

Victorian walnut canterbury with marquetry inlay and carved panel and rising cover. £400

A French-style mahogany standing canterbury with lyre supports, 36cm. high. £230

A Victorian walnut oval canterbury with drawer, on brass castors, 26½ x 18in. £400

A Victorian burr walnut and rosewood canterbury whatnot, 2ft.3in. wide. £540

A Victorian rosewood three division canterbury, 20¼in. wide. £520

A George IV rosewood music canterbury, 20½in. wide. £1,375

A Victorian burr walnut music canterbury of three divisions with spindle turned columns, 1ft.9in. wide. £380

DINING CHAIRS

One of a set of four late
George III inlaid mahogany
side chairs, 34¾in. high.
£3,590

Two of a set of eight William IV
mahogany dining chairs, including a pair of armchairs. £3,000

One of a set of four Victorian
mahogany dining chairs with
trafalgar seats. £390

One of a pair of mid
Georgian mahogany dining
chairs with paper scroll
toprails and pierced splats.
£1,945

One of a pair of Chippendale
mahogany side chairs, Salem,
circa 1770-85, 37in. high.
£15,395

Two of a set of eight George III
mahogany dining chairs, including two open armchairs.
£5,280

A French Art Nouveau oak
dining chair, designed by C.
Plumet and A. Selmersheim.
£340

Two of a set of seven George III
carved mahogany shield back
dining chairs and one later copy,
England, circa 1780. £4,825

One of a pair of Louis XVI
elm chaises with oval backs
and serpentine seats. £1,650

DINING CHAIRS

A carved mahogany Chippendale side chair, Phila., 1760-75, 24in. wide. £169,350

Two of a set of six painted ash bamboo fancy chairs, New England, 1800/15. £1,520

One of a set of eight mahogany dining chairs with drop-in upholstered seats. £2,270

A George I walnut veneered chair with shaped and curved splat back and drop-in seat. £2,100

Two of a set of fourteen George III mahogany ladder-back dining chairs, with leather upholstered seats. £9,180

A George II walnut chair in the manner of Grendey, with drop-in seat. £1,295

One of a set of four George III mahogany side chairs with moulded oval pierced 'umbrella' backs. £4,860

Two of a set of eight Regency mahogany dining chairs with aquamarine linen covered seats. £3,240

A George III mahogany chair with oval padded back and serpentine seat covered in cafe-au-lait silk. £540

DINING CHAIRS

A George III mahogany dining chair with bow shaped toprail and vase shaped splat. £650

One of a set of eight Regency mahogany dining chairs, including an open armchair, with drop-in seats. £2,860

One of a set of ten Regency simulated rosewood dining chairs with caned seats. £1,870

One of an assembled pair of 18th century 'York' maple side chairs, New England, 41in. high. £500

One of a set of six Regency simulated rosewood and parcel gilt dining chairs. £15,120

One of a set of eight oak dining chairs of 17th century design. £2,265

One of a set of six early Georgian walnut and oak dining chairs with drop-in seats. £8,100

One of a pair of Chippendale mahogany slipper chairs, 1750/80, 36½in. high. £760

A Chippendale carved walnut side chair, with shell-carved cabriole legs, Phila., 1760-80. £2,155

DINING CHAIRS

One of a set of eight Regency mahogany dining chairs, and a similar pair of armchairs.
£2,200

One of four Louis XV carved and cream decorated side chairs, having bowed seats on moulded cabriole legs.
£2,600

One of a pair of Chippendale mahogany side chairs, Mass., 1760-90, 36½in. high.
£11,490

One of a pair of George II mahogany side chairs, the seat covered with later petit point floral needlework.
£6,050

A Louis XV beechwood chaise with close-nailed cartouche-shaped back, covered in blue cut-velvet.
£660

One of a set of eight George III mahogany dining chairs, the padded seats covered in close-nailed yellow brocade.
£9,900

One of a set of six mid-Georgian mahogany dining chairs with drop-in needle-work-upholstered seats.
£5,940

One of a set of twelve Harlequin Dutch marquetry dining chairs.   £5,400

One of a set of six oak Lancashire chairs with spindle backs and rush seats.
£1,000

DINING CHAIRS

One of a set of six Regency mahogany dining chairs, the toprails incised with key-pattern and ebonised.
£3,456

One of a pair of mid 18th century rococo walnut chairs, 17in. wide, 38in. high.
£4,535

A George II mahogany dining chair with interlaced gothic pattern and figure of eight splat.
£1,295

One of a pair of George III yellow-painted chairs with gothic-arcaded backs.
£4,535

One of a set of six Regency ebonised and parcel gilt dining chairs with split cane seats and buttoned squabs.
£9,350

A Chippendale mahogany side chair, with a serpentine crest rail, circa 1760/85, 38in. high.
£1,135

One of a set of eight ebonised and parcel gilt dining chairs on sabre legs with drop-in seats, upholstered in pale yellow silk.
£2,050

A Chippendale walnut side chair on cabriole legs with shell carved knees and claw and ball feet, 1760/80.
£11,380

A Queen Anne walnut side chair with balloon shaped seat, 1740/60, 41in. high.
£9,100

DINING CHAIRS

One of a set of four Continental ivory inlaid chairs, 38in. high. £1,845

One of a set of eight white painted frame side chairs covered in late 18th/early 19th century tapestry. £3,500

One of a set of four carved oak dining chairs with padded seats and back. £210

One of a set of five Chippendale-style mahogany dining chairs with acanthus carved top rails. £1,050

One of a set of six Federal-style mahogany dining chairs with shaped crest rails. £590

One of a set of eight late 18th century Dutch neo-classical mahogany dining chairs with bowed upholstered seats. £4,860

One of a set of twelve William IV carved mahogany dining chairs with stuff over seats. £5,600

One of a pair of Louis XV beechwood chaises with cartouche-shaped backs and serpentine seats. £990

An Empire mahogany chaise with padded seat covered in green velour. £310

DINING CHAIRS

A Queen Anne mahogany
side chair with balloon slip
seat, Mass., circa 1770.
£3,560

A Federal carved mahogany
side chair and armchair,
possibly by John Carlile, Jr.,
Rhode Island.   £2,138

Queen Anne walnut side
chair, the yoke crest above
vase form splat, Mass., circa
1730.   £2,780

One of four George II mahogany dining chairs with
front cabriole supports with
pad feet.   £2,090

Two of a set of eight Georgian
mahogany dining chairs with brass
inlaid cresting rails.   £4,000

One of a set of six George
III mahogany dining chairs
with buttoned squabs
covered in yellow silk.
£2,750

One of a pair of George I
walnut chairs with drop-in
needlework seats. £1,650

Two of a set of eleven George III
mahogany dining chairs, including
an open armchair.   £15,120

One of a set of six George III
mahogany dining chairs with
bowed padded seats. £2,700

DINING CHAIRS

One of a set of four mid 18th century oak dining chairs with pierced splat backs. £780

Two of a set of ten Regency rosewood dining chairs, the caned seats with velvet covered squab cushion. £7,020

A Chippendale mahogany side chair with slip seat. Phila., circa 1770. £2,500

One of a set of six black painted Windsor side chairs, each stamped 'J. R. Hunt, Maker', circa 1820. £2,320

Two of a set of eight mahogany ladder back chairs in the Chippendale manner. £1,800

One of a set of eight George III mahogany dining chairs, including two armchairs. £5,615

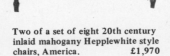

One of a set of six Scottish Regency period mahogany side chairs, seats covered in striped material. £2,500

Two of a set of eight 20th century inlaid mahogany Hepplewhite style chairs, America. £1,970

One of a pair of Country Chippendale walnut side chairs with square slip seats, Penn., circa 1780. £4,720

EASY CHAIRS

A beechwood fauteuil of Louis XV style with seat covered in 18th century gros and petit point needlework. £3,130

Tecno 'P 45' adjustable reclining wing armchair, designed by O. Borsani. £160

A William IV rosewood armchair with button-upholstered tub back and armrests. £1,945

A George III parcel gilt and white painted open armchair with oval back, upholstered in puce silk. £1,100

An upholstered oak armchair with cut out sides, circa 1905, 28¾in. wide. £700

A George III giltwood bergere in the manner of J. Linnell, inscribed 'Roberts 1784' on the frame under the upholstery. £3,455

A Regency mahogany reading chair with deeply buttoned green leather upholstery and yoke shaped toprail. £540

A mid Victorian walnut open armchair, the cartouche-shaped padded back with gros and petit point needlework panel. £880

A Regency mahogany side chair after a design by Thos. Hope, with buttoned scroll back and seat in a moulded frame. £3,740

EASY CHAIRS

A Georgian carved and ebonised elbow chair, in the manner of John Linnell.
£340

One of a pair of cantilever Modernist armchairs, 1930's.
£570

One of a pair of mid 19th century ormolu mounted mahogany bergeres in the Empire style.
£7,560

Early 18th century parcel gilt and cream painted fauteuil with cartouche shaped back.
£810

One of a pair of Regency rosewood tub bergeres with arched padded backs.
£3,780

Mid 19th century walnut salon chair with moulded and pierced rail, and serpentine padded seat.
£660

A Louis XV beige-painted bergere, by J. B. Boulard, with shaped back and padded seat.
£1,730

One of a pair of mid 19th century walnut folding armchairs with suede backs and seats, the frames carved to simulate bamboo.
£2,590

A 17th century and later Flemish walnut open armchair with arched padded back and seat.
£865

EASY CHAIRS

A Gustav Stickley oak office chair with leather back and seat, circa 1907, 36in. high. £2,500

One of a pair of early Victorian rosewood armchairs, each with a spoon-shaped back and serpentine seat, on cabriole legs. £3,080

A Renaissance Revival carved rosewood armchair, attributed to J. Jelliff, N.J., circa 1865, 29in. wide. £1,300

One of a set of six George II giltwood side chairs, the back and seat upholstered in crimson cut velvet, 27in. wide. £124,200

A Regency mahogany open armchair with railed simulated bamboo back and padded arm supports and seat with leather cushion. £920

A 19th century carved mahogany side chair, with spoon shaped back, India, 48½in. high. £345

One of a pair of William and Mary scarlet and gold lacquer X-frame open armchairs, 26½in. wide. £32,400

A tub armchair by Rennie Mackintosh for the Ingram Street Tea Rooms in Glasgow. £3,000

A Regency brass mounted mahogany tub bergere with leather upholstered back, arms and squab cushion. £5,400

58

EASY CHAIRS

A mid Victorian mahogany armchair, upholstered in oxblood buttoned leather. £2,050

Late Victorian mahogany framed armchair with turned legs and arm supports. £120

A Regency giltwood throne armchair, attributed to Morel & Hughes. £21,600

A Regency mahogany tub bergere with cane-filled back and button drop-in seat, stamped HW. £810

A mid Victorian walnut tub armchair with padded back and seat, on cabriole legs. £825

A parcel gilt and beechwood fauteuil of neo-classical design, on spirally-turned tapering legs. £1,430

A Louis XVI stained beech-wood bergere, the back, seat and squab covered in plum velvet. £1,320

A 17th century beechwood X-framed open armchair covered in fragments of contemporary associated tapestry. £4,320

A mid Victorian walnut folding armchair with button upholstered slung seat and back, on sabre legs. £660

EASY CHAIRS

A Victorian mahogany framed horseshoe-back armchair with cabriole front legs.　£200

A mid Victorian easy armchair with buttoned back and seat upholstered in floral cut velvet and green velvet.　£4,105

An early George III giltwood bergere upholstered in aqua-marine silk.　£825

Victorian carved mahogany rocking chair with padded arms.　£250

An inlaid rosewood curule-type armchair, attributed to Pottier and Stymus, circa 1870, 34in. high, 31in. wide.　£765

A Charles I beech open arm-chair, the back and seat upholstered in gold and crimson velvet damask.　£1,510

Chippendale mahogany loll-ing chair, attributed to J. Short, Mass., circa 1780.　£5,555

One of a pair of Regency simulated bronze and parcel gilt bergeres after a design by George Smith, 24in. wide.　£57,200

A George III parcel gilt and white painted open armchair, covered in a blue, white and grey floral brocade.　£715

60

EASY CHAIRS

A George III mahogany
bergere with later brass feet
and castors.   £6,600

A Regency beechwood bergere,
on ring turned tapering legs,
lacking candle arms.   £825

Victorian mahogany par-
lour armchair, circa 1870.
                    £450

A Regency mahogany ber-
gere with moulded arm
supports and fluted tapering legs, the seat re-caned.
                    £865

One of a pair of mid 19th
century ebonised Gothic
Revival armchairs, America,
57in. high.   £625

A William and Mary walnut
open armchair, the back
and seat upholstered in
yellow damask.   £1,730

One of a set of six mid 18th
century Italian parcel gilt
and green painted open armchairs.   £10,450

Mid 19th century Louis XV
style tapestry upholstered
miniature giltwood bergere,
France, 19in. wide. £1,575

A mid 18th century Venetian
parcel gilt and aquamarine
open armchair, the padded
back and seat upholstered in
point d'hongerie velvet.
                  £1,080

ELBOW CHAIRS

A late 18th century Italian walnut open armchair with upholstered seat. £755

One of a pair of early 19th century Gothic open armchairs with later solid seats. £5,615

One of a pair of George III mahogany armchairs with bowed padded seats. £1,430

One of a pair of George III green-painted beechwood open armchairs with shaped drop-in seats. £2,810

A mid 19th century Windsor writing armchair on rockers, 43½in. high. £800

One of six Regency painted elbow chairs, the beech frames with rectangular and canted openwork backs and cane seats. £3,740

One of a set of eight Regency mahogany dining chairs with cane filled seats and sabre legs. £3,890

Fancy wicker armchair, by Heywood Bros. & Co., Mass., 39in. high. £840

A Chippendale mahogany open armchair, circa 1770-85. £8,400

ELBOW CHAIRS

An early Georgian walnut open armchair with drop-in needlework seat. **£650**

One of a pair of Regency painted open armchairs, the later solid seats with squab cusions. **£2,270**

One of a set of eight Chippendale-style mahogany dining chairs. **£1,500**

One of a pair of George III cream and green painted open armchairs, with bowed cane-filled seats. **£1,190**

One of a set of four Italian walnut armchairs in Renaissance style, with leather covered seats. **£1,650**

A Regency mahogany open armchair of gothic style with pierced arcaded back. **£1,295**

A mid 17th century Franco-Flemish walnut armchair with stuffed back and seat. **£1,045**

One of a pair of Federal style mahogany lolling chairs, 41¼in. high. **£2,300**

One of a set of four early Victorian oak open armchairs by Bell & Coupland, Preston. **£7,700**

ELBOW CHAIRS

One of a pair of George III mahogany open armchairs with tapering beaded railed backs. £1,190

A Continental walnut and upholstered armchair, circa 1680, French or Flemish. £395

One of a set of four parcel gilt and green painted side chairs with cane-filled backs and seats, mid 18th century. £3,025

Early 19th century mahogany bergere on reeded front legs. £240

One of a pair of avodire and painted open armchairs, each with a shield-shaped back. £3,080

A laminated mahogany armchair, circa 1900, 45in. high. £355

One of a pair of Italian Empire parcel gilt and cream painted fauteuils with padded backs and seats. £3,450

One of a set of six parcel gilt and simulated rosewood open armchairs of Regency style. £6,480

A mahogany frame open arm elbow library chair in the early Georgian manner by Howard & Sons. £875

ELBOW CHAIRS

A George III mahogany open
armchair with shield-shaped
back and pierced splat.
£1,980

A Charles II oak armchair
with solid seat and turned
front legs, the stretchers
now missing.   £605

A George III mahogany open
armchair, and another similar.
£605

A Charles I oak box-base
armchair, circa 1640,
1ft.10in. wide.   £935

A George III green and gold
lacquer open armchair with
pierced oval wheelback.
£3,025

One of a pair of George II
mahogany hall armchairs,
and a settee, 49in. wide.
£15,120

One of a pair of George III
mahogany library armchairs
covered in close-nailed blue
suede.   £16,500

A late 18th/early 19th century
ash and elm chair with wide
seat and turned legs.   £680

An early Georgian walnut
open armchair, the back and
seat covered in yellow damask.
£1,980

ELBOW CHAIRS

One of a pair of Spanish walnut open armchairs, partly 17th century.
£2,420

One of a pair of Regency mahogany open armchairs, the later caned seats with leather squab cushions.
£5,185

A Charles II walnut open armchair with cane-filled back and seat. £1,945

One of two late 18th century brace-back continuous arm Windsors, 38in. high.
£2,655

Late 19th century Victorian steer horn armchair, upholstered in maroon velvet, America. £910

A green painted bowback Windsor armchair, circa 1780. £2,085

A William and Mary walnut open armchair, with shaped railed splats and padded seat. £810

One of a pair of oak Bentwood open armchairs, each bearing a label 'Patent Pending 25597/1932, Regd Design 781, 637. £340

A Pilgrim Century turned oak armchair, with a rush seat, circa 1670/1710, 42½in. high. £230

ELBOW CHAIRS

A carved walnut armchair, by G. Hunzinger, N.Y., circa 1869, 32¾in. high. £280

One from a set of twelve George III-style mahogany chairs, modern. £1,265

An 18th century Chinese padoukwood open arm elbow chair with cane seat. £1,600

A Windsor ash and maple writing armchair, America, circa 1800, 43in. high. £1,340

One of two Dutch Colonial hardwood burgomaster chairs with drop-in seats. £3,850

One of a pair of early 19th century yew and elm Windsor armchairs. £1,550

Early 19th century comb-back rocker, New England, 39in. high. £360

A Queen Anne maple corner chair with stepped horseshoe shaped back, 1735-65. £610

A child's Lancashire spindle-back wing open arm rocking chair with rush seat. £200

LIBRARY CHAIRS

A rosewood library chair dating from the reign of William IV. £600

A Regency mahogany library bergere upholstered in buttoned pale green leather. £1,540

Late 18th century George III library chair on Marlborough legs, 40in. high. £1,865

A George III mahogany library armchair, the back and seat upholstered in green floral silk. £3,780

One of a pair of George III giltwood library armchairs, upholstered in mustard-yellow cut velvet. £20,900

A George III mahogany library armchair with padded back, arm supports and bowed seat upholstered in maroon damask. £1,870

An early George II mahogany library armchair upholstered in floral yellow damask, on cabriole legs and scrolled feet. £6,160

One of a pair of early George III mahogany library armchairs with padded backs, arm supports and seats. £7,020

One of a pair of George III mahogany library armchairs upholstered in pale grey floral silk. £28,080

LIBRARY CHAIRS

A George III mahogany library armchair with padded back and seat. £3,890

A William IV mahogany library armchair with cane filled back, arms and seat, with leather squab cushions. £1,080

One of a pair of mahogany library armchairs of early George III design. £4,320

One of a pair of early George III mahogany library chairs covered in close-nailed and buttoned yellow damask. £26,400

One of a pair of mid Georgian mahogany library armchairs with padded backs, armrests and seats. £18,360

A late George II mahogany library armchair with serpentine back, circa 1750. £4,180

A George III mahogany library armchair with waved back, arm supports and seat upholstered in black leather. £2,160

A William IV library armchair, the back, arms and seat upholstered in pale green leather. £495

One of two George III mahogany library armchairs with padded backs, arms and seats, one re-railed, one partly re-railed. £2,160

WING CHAIRS

A Queen Anne walnut wing armchair upholstered in olive leather.   £4,860

A Charles II oak sleeping armchair, the hinged back, wings and seat upholstered in raspberry damask.£3,130

A Queen Anne walnut armchair, upholstered in lime green silk.   £2,700

A Queen Anne style easy chair, upholstered in a red, white and blue bargello patterned fabric.   £1,005

A William and Mary walnut wing armchair upholstered in fruiting and floral tapestry.   £10,800

An early Georgian walnut wing armchair with high back, upholstered in close-nailed scarlet velvet.
    £5,280.

A Federal mahogany easy chair, on square tapering legs joined by a box stretcher, New England, 1790-1800.
    £1,835

A George I walnut wing armchair covered in green material.   £4,860

A mid Georgian mahogany wing armchair upholstered in pale yellow floral damask.
    £1,510

WING CHAIRS

A walnut wing armchair with waved seat-rail on cabriole legs. £2,200

A Chippendale style upholstered wing armchair on claw and ball feet. £210

A mid Georgian elm wing armchair with arched back and leather upholstery. £2,375

A George I walnut wing armchair with eared padded back and down-scrolled arms, covered in brown leather. £2,700

A Queen Anne walnut wing armchair with eared padded back, 36½in. wide. £36,720

An early Georgian walnut wing armchair, the back and out-scrolled arms and bowed seat upholstered in floral moquette. £2,420

A Queen Anne walnut wing armchair upholstered in gros point needlework. £7,020

A walnut wing armchair, the seat upholstered in yellow floral damask, on shell cabriole legs and claw and ball feet. £1,190

A George I mahogany easy chair on cabriole legs with slipper feet, 1720-30. £2,140

CHESTS-OF-DRAWERS

A George II mahogany chest with four graduated long drawers, 30in. wide. £1,430

A William and Mary walnut and marquetry chest, circa 1690, 3ft.4in. wide. £4,070

A walnut and oyster-veneered chest decorated and inlaid with boxwood lines, part 18th century, 37in. wide. £2,300

A 19th century mahogany campaign chest, the drawers with brass inset handles, 3ft. wide. £700

A William and Mary painted pine blanket chest, Conn., 1720-40, 41in. wide. £6,170

A Federal inlaid mahogany bowfront chest-of-drawers, New Hampshire, 1790-1810, 40in. wide. £4,310

A William and Mary mulberry and walnut crossbanded chest, circa 1690, 3ft. 2½in. wide. £1,100

Chippendale cherry serpentine chest-of-drawers with old brasses, Conn., circa 1780, 34½in. wide. £4,000

Chippendale tiger maple blanket chest, New England, circa 1780, 36in. wide. £970

CHESTS-OF-DRAWERS

A George II mahogany chest with cast gilt brass drop handles and escutcheons, 96cm. wide. £680

A Country Chippendale maple serpentine chest, New England, circa 1780, 33¼in. wide. £2,770

A Chippendale mahogany bow-front bureau, possibly Rhode Island, circa 1780, 37½in. wide. £4,615

Federal mahogany inlaid bow-front chest with original brass pulls, circa 1790, 40in. wide. £1,610

Chippendale walnut tall chest-of-drawers with old brass pulls, Penn., circa 1780, 38in. wide. £2,665

Federal bird's-eye maple and birch chest-of-drawers, probably New Hampshire, circa 1820, 37¾in. wide. £1,120

A George II mahogany chest on ogee bracket feet, 2ft. 10in. wide, circa 1750. £1,045

Federal inlaid bureau with rectangular maple bow front, New Hampshire, circa 1790, 40⅜in. wide. £2,915

A William and Mary chest-of-drawers, circa 1695, 3ft.2in. wide. £2,750

CHESTS-OF-DRAWERS

A mid Georgian mahogany chest with four graduated drawers on bracket feet, 30in. wide.   £1,835

A William and Mary burr-walnut and crossbanded chest, on later turned feet, circa 1690, 3ft.3in. wide.   £1,265

A Queen Anne tiger maple chest of drawers, New England, circa 1750, 36in. wide.   £2,040

A Chippendale pine chest-of-drawers, New England, 1760-80, 40in. wide.   £570

An 18th century Anglo-Dutch corner dressing chest veneered on oak, 35¾in. wide.   £860

A Chippendale cherrywood chest-of-drawers, 1760/90, 40in. wide.   £1,215

A Chippendale maple tall chest, New England, circa 1770, 36in. wide.   £1,605

A Federal inlaid mahogany and maple veneered chest-of-drawers, probably Boston, 1800-15, 43¾in. wide.   £3,630

A Country Chippendale cherry tall chest on bracket base, New England, circa 1780, 36in. wide. £2,780

CHESTS-OF-DRAWERS

An early 18th century inlaid walnut chest-of-drawers with brass oval drop handles, 35½in. wide.   £4,400

A William and Mary walnut chest with ebonised stringing with oval plaque to top, 39in. wide.   £940

A Chippendale mahogany chest-of-drawers, New England, 1760-80, 42in. wide.   £1,580

A William and Mary marquetry and oyster walnut chest, 39in. wide.   £5,500

A George II Cuban mahogany chest-of-drawers with original brass furniture, 33in. wide.   £2,050

George II mahogany bachelor's chest, the top with a baize-lined dressing slide, 31in. wide.   £1,320

A Country Chippendale cherry grain painted tall chest, New England, circa 1800, 37in. wide. £1,805

A George II walnut chest of four graduated long drawers, 2ft.9in. wide, circa 1730, feet replaced. £4,400

Chippendale maple tall chest with six thumb moulded drawers, New England, circa 1770, 38in. wide.   £1,430

CHESTS-OF-DRAWERS

A George III mahogany chest with four graduated long drawers on ogee bracket feet, 38in. wide. £1,295

A Jacobean style oak and walnut chest fitted with four long drawers, 41in. wide. £990

A Chippendale mahogany chest-of-drawers, New England, 1780-1800, 33½in. wide. £3,015

A Queen Anne painted pine blanket chest, circa 1740, 37¼in. wide. £590

Late 19th century wood tansu in two parts, 118.5cm. wide. £990

A George III mahogany chest of four long graduated drawers, 31in. wide. £1,540

Chippendale tiger maple chest, New England, circa 1780, 37in. wide. £4,545

A Chippendale maple tall chest-of-drawers, New England, circa 1760, 36in. wide. £1,485

A Chippendale maple chest-of-drawers on bracket feet, New England, circa 1770, 34in. wide. £2,325

CHESTS-OF-DRAWERS

A Chippendale mahogany chest-of-drawers, 1765-85, 40in. wide.   £2,140

A Charles II walnut chest, of two short and three long drawers, 3ft.3in. wide, circa 1680.   £880

A Chippendale birch chest-of-drawers on bracket feet, 38½in. wide.   £1,300

A George III mahogany serpentine fronted chest-of-drawers with chased brass handles, 36½in. wide.   £2,900

A late Georgian mahogany bowfront chest crossbanded and inlaid with boxwood lines, 36in. wide.   £500

A mahogany bachelor's chest with crossbanded rounded rectangular top, basically 18th century, 30in. wide. £14,300

An early George III mahogany chest on later ogee bracket feet, 31½in. wide.   £1,430

A tulipwood veneered chest of six drawers, in the French manner, with Sevres type floral plaques, 2ft.6in. wide.   £1,080

Mid 19th century Napoleon III carved mahogany chest-of-drawers, 51½in. wide. £310

CHESTS-ON-CHESTS

A Charles II walnut and marquetry cabinet on chest, on later bracket feet, 49½in. wide. £8,640

An 18th century Continental mahogany chest-on-chest, 43in. wide. £2,330

A Chippendale cherrywood chest-on-chest, in two sections, 1760/80, 41in. wide. £3,415

A Chippendale maple chest-on-chest, in two parts, New England, 1760-90, 37½in. wide. £17,420

A George III mahogany tallboy with figured front and original brass handles, 47in. wide. £6,050

A James Bartram Chippendale mahogany chest-on-chest, in two sections, circa 1750/70, 44½in. wide. £75,860

A Chippendale maple chest-on-chest, in two parts, probably New Hampshire, 1760-90, 38½in. wide. £8,710

A Chippendale inlaid walnut tall chest-of-drawers, Penn., 1760-90, 44½in. wide. £2,320

A George III mahogany secretaire tallboy, 42½in. wide, 72½in. high. £2,090

FURNITURE

CHESTS-ON-CHESTS

'A George I walnut secretaire tallboy on shaped bracket feet, circa 1720, 3ft.5½in. wide. £7,700

A George III mahogany secretaire chest-on-chest, 3ft.7½in. wide, circa 1760. £1,320

A George III mahogany tallboy with key-patterned cornice, 44½in. wide. £2,375

Chippendale cherry chest-on-chest, New England, circa 1770, 38in. wide. £2,255

A Queen Anne walnut and burr walnut tallboy, the lower part with a secretaire drawer, 43in. wide. £12,960

A Chippendale walnut chest-on-chest on ogee bracket feet, 44in. wide, 1760-90. £25,970

A George III mahogany tallboy, the base fitted with a secretaire drawer, 44in. wide. £2,590

A Chippendale maple tall chest, Rhode Island, circa 1780, 35.3/8in. wide. £2,055

A George III mahogany tallboy with three short and six long drawers, 49in. wide. £4,105

79

CHESTS-ON-CHESTS

A George I walnut secretaire tallboy, circa 1720, 3ft. 6in. wide. £5,720

A George III mahogany chest-on-chest, circa 1770, 3ft.6in. wide. £1,155

A George III mahogany chest-on-chest, circa 1760, 3ft.8in. wide. £1,925

A George I walnut tallboy with moulded cornice, 45½in. wide. £5,500

A George III mahogany tallboy on ogee bracket feet, 43¾in. wide. £2,750

An early Georgian walnut tallboy on later bracket feet, 41½in. wide. £5,500

Chippendale cherry flat top chest-on-chest, Conn., circa 1770, 38¼in. wide. £7,665

A George III mahogany chest-on-chest, 3ft.7½in. wide, circa 1765. £1,045

A mid Georgian mahogany tallboy on ogee bracket feet, 44in. wide, 73in. high. £1,295

CHEST-ON-CHESTS

An early Georgian walnut and oak tallboy on bracket feet, 41½in. wide. £1,835

A Queen Anne walnut tallboy with chamfered cavetto cornice, 42in. wide. £23,100.

A George III mahogany tallboy with key-pattern cornice, 44½in. wide. £1,980

A Chippendale maple chest on-chest, circa 1770-85, 38in. wide. £2,900

A George III mahogany tallboy, 46in. wide. £1,730

A William and Mary oyster-veneered walnut chest-on-chest, 43½in. wide. £3,025

A George III mahogany serpentine front tallboy chest on ogee bracket feet, 4ft. overall. £4,700

Georgian mahogany chest-on-chest, 1790. £1,280

A Chippendale cherrywood chest-on-chest, in two sections, 1765-85, 38½in. wide. £5,730

CHESTS-ON-STANDS

A Queen Anne maple highboy, New Jersey, circa 1730, 37in. wide. £5,900

A Queen Anne cherrywood bonnet top high chest, circa 1740-70, 41in. wide. £19,270

A Chippendale maple highboy with original brasses, circa 1760, 38in. wide. £6,945

A Queen Anne walnut chest-on-stand with two short and three graduated long drawers on the upper chest, 43in. wide. £1,730

A Queen Anne walnut chest on frame, in two sections, Penn., 1750-80, 69in. high. £4,585

A Queen Anne maple high chest-of-drawers, in two sections, Mass., 1740/60, 36in. wide. £7,205

A William and Mary style burr walnut veneered chest-on-stand inlaid with geometric chequered boxwood lines, 44in. wide. £1,400

A William and Mary walnut and marquetry chest-on-stand, 38½in. wide. £2,640

A William and Mary kingwood oyster veneered and rosewood banded chest-on-stand, the stand circa 1840, 49½in. wide. £3,300

CHESTS-ON-STANDS

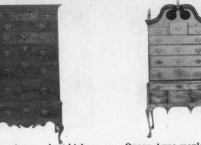

A Queen Anne walnut high chest on frame, 1750-70, 40½in. wide. £7,255

Queen Anne maple bonnet top highboy, New England, circa 1760, 38in. wide. £2,775

A Queen Anne cherrywood highboy, probably Wethersfield, Conn., circa 1740-65, 37½in. wide. £10,695

A William and Mary birch high chest-of-drawers, in two sections, 1710-20, 44in. wide. £7,255

A Queen Anne oak grain painted chest on frame, England, circa 1730, 38in. wide. £2,110

A Queen Anne burl and walnut veneer highboy, Mass., circa 1740, 61¼in. high. £11,265

A William and Mary maple and burl walnut veneer highboy, Mass., circa 1730, 39½in. wide. £2,745

An early 18th century walnut chest-on-stand, the base with one long drawer, 3ft.2in. wide. £550

A walnut chest-on-stand, the base with six various sized drawers, 42in. wide. £2,160

CHESTS-ON-STANDS

A Queen Anne burr walnut chest-on-stand with feather banded top, 40¾in. wide. £2,420

Queen Anne maple highboy with five graduated drawers, one long drawer and three split drawers, circa 1740, 75¼in. high. £15,970

A Queen Anne walnut chest-on-stand inlaid with fruitwood compass medallions, 42in. wide. £1,620

A Queen Anne walnut chest-on-stand with an ogee cornice above a cushion drawer, 39in. wide. £2,200

A walnut chest-on-stand, the cupboard door enclosing a fitted interior, flanked by six drawers, 37½in. wide. £1,135

A Queen Anne walnut veneer high chest-of-drawers, 1735-50, 40in. wide. £3,665

A George II walnut chest-on-stand on later cabriole supports, 40in. wide. £1,650

A floral marquetry William and Mary veneered chest-of-drawers, 3ft.4in. wide. £6,500

A George II walnut tallboy with a cavetto cornice, 40in. wide. £1,925

CHESTS-ON-STANDS

A Queen Anne walnut chest-on-stand with two short and three graduated long drawers, 40in. wide.   £6,600

A Queen Anne cherrywood high chest of drawers, in two sections, circa 1740-70, 39in. wide.   £6,050

An oak chest of two long drawers raised on a stand having six barley-twist legs, 3ft.2in. wide.   £380

Queen Anne tiger maple highboy on cabriole legs, Massa., circa 1740, 69in. high.   £11,110

A William and Mary walnut chest-on-stand with two short and three long graduated drawers, 38½in. wide. £1,320

A George I walnut and herringbone crossbanded chest-on-stand, 40in. wide.   £3,025

A Queen Anne cherrywood high chest-of-drawers, Long Island, 1735-70, 40½in. wide.   £7,180

A Queen Anne style walnut veneered highboy on hipped cabriole legs with Spanish type feet, England, 62¼in. high.   £980

A George I walnut and elm chest-on-stand, 38½in. wide.   £2,090

CHIFFONIERS

One of a pair of late Victorian ebonised chiffoniers banded with amboyna, 35¾in. wide. £2,200

A rococo Revival rosewood veneered etagere, America, circa 1860, 51in. wide. £910

A Regency period mahogany chiffonier, the drawers with brass knob handles, 3ft.3in. wide. £1,850

A Regency mahogany chiffonier, the two-tiered superstructure with baluster supports and gallery, 24in. wide. £1,760

A mid 19th century rosewood secretaire chiffonier of reverse breakfront form, 7ft.2in. wide. £1,450

A Regency rosewood secretaire chiffonier with shelf and mirror superstructure, 27in. wide. £650

A George IV rosewood chiffonier, the shelved back inset with a mirror plate, 44in. wide. £850

A Renaissance Revival walnut carved sideboard, the panelled back with two oval mirrors, possibly New York, circa 1860, 89½in. high. £2,130

Early 19th century rosewood chiffonier with two frieze drawers above two panelled doors. £460

CHIFFONIERS

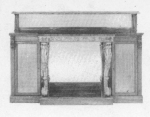

An early Victorian rosewood chiffonier, stamped W. Stratford, 50in. wide. £600

A William IV rosewood and parcel gilt breakfront chiffonier, the doors filled with lime-green silk pleats, 70in. wide. £2,810

A Regency ebonised maple-wood and bois clair chiffonier with two open shelves, 34in. wide. £2,810

A William IV figured mahogany chiffonier with scroll carved bracket supports, 3ft. 10in. wide. £660

A Victorian walnut inlaid chiffonier with triple arched mirror back, 5ft. wide. £525

A Regency rosewood chiffonier with small canopy back and on four bun feet, 36in. wide. £700

An early Victorian mahogany chiffonier, the top with a three-quarter galleried superstructure, 40in. wide. £800

A William IV mahogany chiffonier, the base with two recessed mirror panelled doors, 42in. wide. £1,250

One of a pair of mid Victorian satinwood, purpleheart and gilt metal mounted chiffoniers applied with blue Wedgwood plaques. 42in. wide. £6,480

CLOTHES PRESSES

A George III satinwood
clothes press, the sides crossbanded with rosewood, 51½in.
wide, 77¼in. high.   £15,400

A Regency mahogany clothes
press, the panelled doors
enclosing four slides and two
drawers, 56½in. wide. £2,640

A George III fiddleback
mahogany serpentine clothes
press, 54in. wide.   £19,440

A George III satinwood
clothes press, the cupboard
doors enclosing five slides,
49½in. wide.   £3,890

A George III mahogany
breakfront clothes press,
6ft.6in. wide, circa 1770,
later pediments.   £2,200

A George II mahogany
clothes press, the cornice
with foliate and egg-and-dart
border, 53in. wide. £27,000

An early George III sycamore
clothes press on re-inforced
ogee bracket feet, 45½in.
wide.   £1,945

A George III mahogany
clothes press on bracket
feet, 50in. wide, 71in.
high.   £970

A late 18th century maho-
gany clothes press, the drawers with original oval brass
plates, 4ft. wide.   £1,600

COMMODE CHESTS

An ormolu mounted king-
wood commode of Louis XV--
style with serpentine breccia
marble top, 48in. wide.
£1,980

A Dutch mahogany and
marquetry commode on
later feet, 49in. wide.
£4,620

One of a pair of George III
kingwood commodes in the
French style, 50in. wide.
£99,000

An ormolu mounted king-
wood and fruitwood com-
mode of Louis XVI-style,
34¾in. wide.   £2,160

A George III mahogany small
commode, the serpentine top
geometrically veneered and
crossbanded, 29½in. wide.
£5,280

A Louis XV-style rosewood,
kingwood and marquetry inlaid serpentine front commode chest, 2ft.11¼in. wide.
£600

A George III mahogany
serpentine commode with
four graduated long drawers,
46½in. wide.   £9,720

Mid 18th century Danish
rosewood and parcel gilt
commode with white
marble top, 28in. wide.
£2,050

A George II mahogany dressing
commode with lobed serpentine top and a drawer above a
central cupboard, 55½in. wide.
£11,880

COMMODE CHESTS

A directoire gilt metal mounted mahogany commode on turned tapering feet, 50in. wide. £2,810

An Italian walnut and marquetry commode in the style of Maggiolini, 45in. wide. £1,945

An 18th century Italian walnut serpentine commode, fitted with three long drawers outlined in fruitwood, 51½in. wide. £2,160

A George III satinwood commode crossbanded with rosewood and inlaid with amaranth bands, 47¼in. wide. £8,100

A Louis XV kingwood and marquetry miniature commode, the serpentine top inlaid with a musical trophy, 19½in. wide. £1,295

A George III cream and black painted commode on parcel gilt square tapering fluted legs, 62in. wide. £16,200

An Edwardian painted satinwood commode with D-shaped top inlaid with a halved bat's wing motif, 51in. wide. £3,455

A George III satinwood and marquetry commode in the French style, 45in. wide. £28,080

One of a pair of satinwood commodes crossbanded in rosewood with serpentine tops, 33½in. wide. £5,615

COMMODE CHESTS

A Louis XV style kingwood and rosewood bombe commode, circa 1900, 4ft. 5in. wide. £570

Late 17th/early 18th century Louis XIV harewood and mahogany commode, 51¼in. long. £2,070

An early George I mahogany commode of concave bombe outline, 39in. wide. £30,240

Mid 18th century Portuguese rosewood commode of serpentine outlines with boxwood stringing, 51 in. wide. £3,300

A French serpentine fronted commode chest with marble top, 37in. wide. £850

Late 17th century Italian rosewood commode profusely inlaid with ivory, mother-of-pearl and pewter, 60in. wide. £4,950

A mid 18th century French provincial carved, painted and gilded wood commode, 37½in. wide. £280

Late Empire figured mahogany marble top commode, circa 1830, 47¾in. wide. £765

A George III satinwood commode with eared oval top, 43in. wide. £9,720

COMMODE CHESTS

A George III mahogany serpentine commode, 50½in. wide. £6,050

An 18th century Dutch coromandel and satinwood veneered serpentine commode of slight bombe outline, 1.20m. wide. £1,600

An 18th century Maltese walnut veneered serpentine commode, 5ft.5in. wide. £1,200

A late 18th century walnut crossbanded and parquetry demi-lune commode in the Louis XVI taste, 1.04m. wide, possibly Italian. £3,800

A D-shaped figured oak commode with two panelled doors on gadrooned bun feet, 41½in. wide. £1,000

A George III mahogany veneered demi-lune commode, crossbanded, 3ft.7in. wide. £800

A Dutch mahogany and marquetry commode of bombe form with shaped serpentine top, 35in. wide. £3,520

One of a pair of South German walnut and crossbanded commodes, circa 1720, 2ft.1in. wide. £3,520

A Dutch ormolu mounted mahogany and marquetry commode on cabriole legs. £3,080

COMMODE CHESTS

A George III mahogany commode with crossbanded hinged rectangular top, 50in. wide. £4,320

An ormolu mounted kingwood and marquetry commode of Louis XVI design, with breakfront Carrara marble top, stamped five times Wassmus, 50in. wide. £3,520

A George III mahogany commode with serpentine top above a slide, 45in. wide. £10,260

An ormolu mounted kingwood and tulipwood breakfront commode with moulded breccia marble top, 38in. wide. £2,375

A Louis XV style bombe front Dutch commode with a white marble slab top, 22in. wide. £2,800

One of a pair of South German walnut and fruitwood parquetry commodes, late 18th century, 51½in. wide. £15,120

A 20th century inlaid fruitwood demi-lune commode, with semi-circular variegated onyx top, 48in. wide. £835

An ormolu mounted kingwood and floral marquetry bombe commode of Louis XV style, 51½in. wide. £2,050

One of a pair of George III satinwood, sycamore and marquetry commodes, 46in. wide. £21,600

COMMODES & POT CUPBOARDS

A late 18th century mahogany commode with tambour front and tray top. 20½in. wide.　　　　£300

Victorian mahogany pot cupboard with marble top.
　　　　£110

An early George III mahogany bedside cupboard, 22in. wide.　　　£1,320

An early 19th century flame mahogany pot cupboard with a figured marble top.
　　　　£125

Victorian walnut pot cupboard, circa 1860.
　　　　£85

One of a pair of Biedermeier mahogany bedside cupboards with hinged tops, 22in. wide.
　　　　£18,360

A George III mahogany bowfront bedside commode, 21in. wide.　　　£900

A Georgian mahogany enclosed washstand/commode with fold-over top, rising mirror and fitted compartments and basin, 18in. wide.　　　£605

George III mahogany tray top commode with cupboard above sliding drawer, 20in. wide.　　　£280

George III mahogany tray-top night cupboard, 1ft.8in. wide. £500

One of a pair of late 18th century North Italian, Milanese, walnut and ivory bedside commodes, 24¼in. wide. £11,000

A George III mahogany bedside commode with rectangular tray top, 21in. wide. £660

A Biedermeier mahogany pedestal cupboard with D-shaped top and frieze drawer above a cupboard door and base drawer, 23½in. wide. £660

A pair of walnut bedside tables with rectangular tops and waved three-quarter galleries, 16¼in. wide. £2,420

A Biedermeier mahogany pedestal cabinet, the swivelling door enclosing three shelves, 25½in. wide. £660

A Renaissance Revival walnut demi-commode, 20in. wide. £485

A set of Regency mahogany bedside steps with three leather lined treads, a door and a drawer, 28½in. wide. £1,210

Table de nuit, Continental, brass inlaid with a drawer, cupboard and marble top, 1ft.8in. wide. £420

CORNER CUPBOARDS

A Federal walnut corner cupboard, probably Kentucky, 1800-20, 50in. wide. £1,755

George III mahogany bow-front corner cabinet, 44in. high. £420

A 19th century Continental painted corner cupboard, 81in. high, 41in. wide. £2,510

A Federal cherrywood corner cupboard in two sections, circa 1820-60, 42in. wide. £2,090

A Federal cherrywood corner cupboard, American, 1790/1810, 50½in. wide. £1,820

A Chippendale pine corner cupboard, 1760-90, 78½in. high. £3,665

A cherry corner cupboard with clock, Penn., circa 1815, 83in. high. £1,690

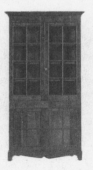

A late Chippendale cherry-wood corner cupboard, American, circa 1785/1810, 45in. wide. £2,275

A Country Federal cherry corner cupboard, Penn., circa 1820, 56½in. wide. £820

CORNER CUPBOARDS

A George III lacquered bow-front corner cupboard, 23½in. wide. £440

A Dutch walnut standing corner cabinet with a domed cornice, 4ft.3in. wide, circa 1740. £2,530

Late 18th century double oak corner cupboard with flat front and four panel doors, 30in. wide. £1,325

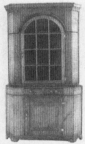

Pine corner cupboard, New England, 48in. wide, circa 1780. £1,680

A mahogany inlaid corner cupboard with glazed astragal door. £260

George III mahogany bow-fronted hanging corner cupboard, 3ft.2in. high. £450

Grain painted pine and poplar corner cupboard, possibly Pennsylvania, circa 1830, 83in. high, 55½in. wide. £2,185

A Chippendale pine hanging corner cupboard, Penn., 1760-85, 46in. high, 26½in. wide. £1,000

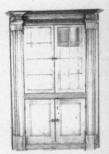

Federal pine corner cupboard, possibly Penn., circa 1820, 56in. wide. £1,400

COURT CUPBOARDS

A 17th century oak court cupboard, 6ft. wide. £900

A small oak court cupboard, basically early 17th century, 27½in. wide. £6,600

A Tudor-style carved oak court cupboard, possibly late 17th century, England, 92½in. wide. £1,485

A Georgian Welsh oak duo-darn, the cornice with two acorn shape pendant finials, 51in. wide. £935

A 17th century oak court cupboard with original brass hinges and escutcheons. £1,300

A walnut court cupboard, in the manner of A. W. Pugin, 147cm. wide. £880

An early 17th century James I inlaid oak court cupboard, 49in. wide. £3,345

Early 18th century oak court cupboard, the doors with ivory escutcheons, 56in. wide. £1,055

A 17th century carved oak court cupboard with moulded cornice, 5ft.2in. wide. £760

CRADLES

A Regency mahogany frame caned side baby's cot with hood, swinging on brass brackets, 3ft.5in. £300

A 17th century oak cradle with arched hood, 40in. wide. £970

A Queen Anne oak cradle with fielded panelled construction, 3ft.3in. long, circa 1705. £450

A Victorian mahogany cradle with swan neck head on turned supports. £780

Late 19th century ebonised Bentwood cradle, Europe, 52in. long. £625

An oak cradle with turned finials, bearing the carved date 1739, 36in. long. £500

A 17th century Flemish oak fruitwood and marquetry cradle, 40in. wide. £970

A George III painted cradle with ogee-arched hood and cane-filled sides, 41in. long. £830

Child's metal cot by Theodore Lambert, 1910, 133cm. long. £270

CREDENZAS

Inlaid walnut veneered serpentine side cabinet with brass mouldings, circa 1850, 6ft.7½in. wide. £3,190

An Exhibition period walnut credenza, the two bow-shaped ends with fitted shelves, 60in. wide. £3,500

A Victorian boxwood banded walnut breakfront credenza with gilt metal mounts, 165cm. wide. £750

Victorian gilt bronze and porcelain mounted walnut side cabinet, circa 1860, 59½in. wide. £915

Italian Renaissance 16th century walnut credenza with D-shaped top, 73in. wide. £535

A Victorian ebonised side cabinet with gilt metal and porcelain mounts, 70in. wide. £550

A Victorian walnut cabinet of serpentine shape with astragal glazed doors, 5ft. 6in. wide. £960

French boulle ebonised and ormolu mounted meuble d'appui, circa 1860, 5ft. wide. £770

Renaissance Revival burl veneer and ebonised wood sideboard cabinet, America, circa 1865, 53in. wide. £1,035

CREDENZAS

A burr-walnut and thuya-wood side cabinet, late 1850's, 6ft.2in. wide. £2,750

A Victorian burr walnut and floral marquetry credenza, 6ft.3in. wide. £2,600

19th century gilt mounted burr walnut credenza. £825

A walnut credenza, the centre cupboard doors inset with Sevres panels flanked by two domed glass fronted cupboards. £1,500

A Victorian walnut side cabinet of D-shape with breakfront outline and bowed glazed sides, 59½in. wide. £770

Mid 19th century Renaissance Revival rosewood credenza, America, 56in. long. £920

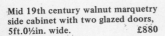

Mid 19th century walnut marquetry side cabinet with two glazed doors, 5ft.0½in. wide. £880

A 19th century walnut, porcelain and gilt metal mounted credenza with mirror back, 182cm. wide. £1,350

French 19th century ebonised mahogany boulle side cabinet. £530

Mid 18th century French
provincial oak cupboard,
the doors partly filled
with wire, 47in. wide.
£2,160

A 17th century Flemish oak
cupboard, the lower part
with a drawer with lion mask
corbels, 55in. wide.   £2,310

An early George III maho-
gany cupboard with original
brass handles, 44in. wide.
£1,650

A butternut and pine cup-
board on tall bracket feet,
New England or Canada,
49in. wide.   £575

Late 17th/early 18th century
oak tack cupboard/settle
with shoe foot trestle base,
73½in. high.   £895

An 18th century Chippen-
dale poplar kas, Hudson
Valley, New York, 56in.
wide.   £1,310

Georgian pine housekeeper's
cupboard, 1790.   £680

A late 18th century housekeeper's cupboard in oak
mahogany crossbanded, 6ft.
6in. wide.   £1,250

Georgian pine housekeeper's
press, 1790.   £520

CUPBOARDS

A Spanish elm cupboard with two doors pierced with gothic lancets, 25in. wide. £5,280

A 17th century Flemish rosewood, oak, ebonised and tortoiseshell cupboard, 64½in. wide. £2,700

A Flemish 17th century oak standing cupboard, 2ft.4½in. wide. £1,430

An 18th century carved pine tall cupboard on replaced ball feet, 44in. wide. £700

An English oak corner buffet, circa 1900, 111cm. wide. £215

A Federal pine step back cupboard, New England, circa 1810, 51in. wide. £1,460

Two-part poplar cupboard, the drawers with brass bail handles, New Jersey, circa 1810, 45in. wide. £1,800

An 18th century oak cupboard having a moulded cornice and double doors with shaped and fielded panels, 22in. wide. £850

Early 19th century oak, mahogany cupboard on bracket feet, 50in. wide. £300

CUPBOARDS

A 19th century American
pine step-back cupboard,
54 in. wide.   £1,350

An 18th century oak bonnetiere, probably Austrian,
29in. wide.   £1,210

A 17th century Flemish oak
press in two parts, 53½in.
wide.   £2,640

An 18th century gumwood
kas, in three sections, Long
Island, N.Y., 74½in. wide.
    £4,355

Federal cherry and mahogany
veneer mantel cupboard,
Penn., circa 1820, 13½in.
wide.   £470

An early 16th century Gothic
oak hutch cupboard or aumbry, 3ft.4½in. wide.   £5,170

Late 17th/18th century
French provincial oak
bonnetiere, 41in. wide.
    £605

A Charles II large chest in
oak and walnut veneered
with snakewood and ebony,
in three sections, 50in. wide.
    £2,420

Late 17th century Flemish
oak cupboard on later
bun feet, 46½in. wide.
    £1,540

CUPBOARDS

A 17th century oak cupboard of rectangular form with plank top, 114cm. wide. £800

Painted pine chimney cupboard, Mass., circa 1810, 25in. wide, 78in. high. £3,985

One of a pair of Austrian oak and leaded glass cupboards, 197.9cm. high, 103.6cm. wide. £860

An oak cupboard, partly 16th century with restorations, 35in. wide. £3,850

A Federal tiger maple cupboard with two glazed doors, 1800-10, 54½in. wide. £2,900

An early 17th century oak food cupboard on turned legs and platform stretcher, 50¼in. wide. £3,455

A mid 18th century mahogany press cupboard with dentil cornice, 3ft.8in. wide. £825

A pine step back cupboard, New England, circa 1800, 58½in. wide. £1,350

A 17th/18th century Italian pine and marquetry cupboard inlaid in walnut and sycamore, 30in. wide. £990

Late 18th century pine pewter cupboard, America, 41in. wide.   £4,750

A late Gothic oak hutch cupboard or aumbry, 3ft. 6in. wide.   £2,640.

A grain painted walnut cupboard, Penn., circa 1820, 82½in. wide.   £810

An oak and fruitwood food cupboard inlaid with geometric lozenge patterns, late 16th/early 17th century, 35¾in. wide.   £4,180

A small painted pine cupboard with four interior shelves, circa 1810, 25¼in. wide.   £1,555

A partly 18th century oak cupboard on bracket feet, 62in. wide.   £1,870

A 16th/17th century Spanish walnut cupboard with two pairs of panelled doors, 37½in. wide.   £2,530

A William and Mary gumwood kas in two sections, New York, 1725-55, 54in. wide.   £2,755

A green painted pine blanket chest/cupboard with lift top, probably Long Island, circa 1785/1825, 43½in. wide.   £2,050

DAVENPORTS

A rosewood and marquetry inlaid davenport, in the manner of T. Turner of Manchester. £800

Victorian carved and brass inlaid mahogany davenport desk, America, 19th century, 29¼in. wide. £675

An early Victorian oak davenport, with hinged leather lined writing panel and four long graduated drawers, 21½in. wide. £500

A Regency mahogany davenport with sliding leather lined sloping flap, enclosing a fitted interior, 20in. wide. £4,180

Early Victorian burr walnut davenport with sliding top, after a design by W. Smee & Sons, London, circa 1850, 1ft.10in. wide. £1,800

A Victorian walnut davenport, with pierced brass gallery and rising surface, 2ft.10in. wide. £775

An early Victorian rosewood davenport with pierced three-quarter gallery, with Bramah locks, 21¼in. wide. £1,980

A mid Victorian burr walnut davenport with serpentine piano lid, 39in. wide. £1,250

A George IV pollard oak davenport with three-quarter pierced brass gallery and leather lined flap, 19½in. wide. £1,870

FURNITURE

DAVENPORTS

A George IV rosewood veneered davenport, the sliding top with a pierced brass gallery, 19.5in. wide. £920

A mid Victorian mahogany davenport of gothic style, 30in. wide. £2,640

A Victorian walnut davenport, with fret gallery above a writing slide and two small drawers, four side drawers, 22in. wide. £1,450

Victorian rosewood davenport, sloping top, fitted interior and four drawers. £700

Victorian ebonised davenport with maple banding and incised decoration. £310

A Victorian walnut davenport, the rectangular coffered top fitted with a sprung stationery compartment. £1,700

A Victorian burr walnut veneered piano top davenport with fitted interior, 22in. wide. £1,200

A 19th century Irish inlaid yew davenport with fitted interior, 25½in. wide. £2,200

A Victorian walnut davenport with ebony inlay and hinged lid to stationery compartment, 21in. wide. £400

DAVENPORTS

Victorian walnut davenport with shaped legs, 1860. £940

Victorian mahogany davenport with galleried stationery box, 22in. wide. £380

A Regency davenport with gilt metal three-quarter pierced gallery, 20½in. wide. £1,945

A mid Victorian gilt and mother-of-pearl, black japanned, papier mache davenport on bun feet, 27in. wide. £1,945

A rosewood davenport with balustrade gallery, 23in. wide. £850

A Killarney arbutus wood davenport inlaid with architectural subject ovals, 31½in. wide. £4,000

An inlaid burr walnut davenport with sycamore interior, late 19th century. £825

A Regency calamander wood davenport, the turned feet with brass castors, 21¼in. wide, circa 1820. £1,100

An inlaid burr walnut davenport with three-quarter pierced gallery, 24¾in. wide. £1,945

DAVENPORTS

A Victorian burr walnut and ebonised harlequin davenport, 1ft.11in. wide, circa 1870.   £1,540

An early Victorian figured walnut davenport, the surprise pop-up top with three-quarter gallery, 22½in. wide.   £1,500

Regency rosewood davenport with spindle turned gallery, circa 1815, 1ft.8in. wide.   £970

Mid 19th century Victorian burl walnut davenport desk, 23in. wide.   £520

A Victorian rosewood davenport, the rectangular top with a three-quarter gallery, 24in. wide.   £780

A Regency rosewood davenport with three-quarter gilt metal gallery and leather lined flap, 20½in. wide.   £2,200

A Victorian figured walnut davenport with serpentine front with hinged sloping writing surface, 54cm. wide.   £500

A Victorian burr walnut davenport with a sliding hinged writing slope, 33in. high.   £740

A Victorian burr walnut davenport with a rear hinged stationery compartment, 1ft.11in. wide, circa 1850.   £600

DESKS

A Sheraton period faded mahogany roll-top pedestal desk fitted with brass swan-neck handles, 3ft. 10in. wide. **£1,900**

A George III mahogany architect's desk with rectangular sloping double-flap top, 54in. wide. **£2,420**

A late George III mahogany library desk with pierced gallery and Vitruvian scroll frieze, the plinth base 72in. diam. **£24,840**

A lady's oak desk with fall-front, circa 1890, 28½in. wide. **£320**

A Japanese red and black lacquer cylinder pedestal desk, inlaid with mother-of-pearl and inset with gold lacquer panels, 1.04. wide. **£4,600**

Victorian oak fall front desk, 1880. **£90**

Victorian oak desk with leather top, 1880. **£150**

A Louis XVI small kingwood desk or jewel cabinet banded in purple heart, 15 x 39in. high. **£27,000**

A Queen Anne walnut desk with hinged slant lid, 1740-60, 30½in. wide. **£2,290**

DESKS

A Chippendale pine standing desk, New England, 1780-1810, 30½in. wide.   £765

A George III satinwood cylinder desk with tambour shutter enclosing a fitted interior, 39¼in. wide.
£28,600

A lady's Federal mahogany tambour front writing desk, 32¾in. wide.   £480

A Federal inlaid mahogany writing desk, 1790-1810, 29in. wide.   £2,000

Federal mahogany and mahogany veneer desk, possibly New York, circa 1820, 50½in. wide.   £400

A Federal inlaid mahogany writing desk, with hinged lid, 1790-1810, 29.7/8in. wide.   £1,155

A Gustav Stickley drop-front desk, the doors opening to reveal a fitted interior, circa 1906, 38in. wide.   £1,665

A Victorian walnut roll-top desk, Winneberger, Penn., circa 1890, 40½in. wide.
£710

A Federal cherrywood writing desk, 1800-15, 30½in. wide.   £965

DESKS

A Maurice Dufrene semi-circular wooden desk, 31in. high, and a chair upholstered in red velvet, 32in. high, signed and dated 1935. £2,800

Edwardian oak fall front desk cabinet, 1910.   £90

A Regency writing desk in the manner of Gillows, the drawer with Bramah lock.
£3,130

An Empire mahogany desk with ten leathered compartments and leather lined easel writing surface, 57in. wide.   £3,780

Late 19th century oak tambour top desk.   £175

Mid 19th century barrel roll desk with four ogee drawers, 57in. wide.
£2,165

A rococo walnut marquetry lady's desk, bombe and serpentine case with fall-front, Italy, 31in. wide.   £980

A 19th century George III style inlaid mahogany writing desk, America, 46in. wide.
£655

A sailor made ship's desk, constructed by a sailor on the Bark Messenger, circa 1850, 23½in. wide.
£1,390

DISPLAY CABINETS

Late 18th century Nether-lands rococo mahogany mar-quetry cabinet, 56in. wide.
£5,420

An Eastern carved hardwood display cabinet, 130cm. wide. £2,000

An Art Nouveau inlaid maho-gany vitrine, 114.7cm. wide.
£700

An Art Nouveau mahogany breakfront cabinet, pro-bably made by Liberty, circa 1898, 139cm. wide.
£550

A Victorian rococo style mahogany side cabinet with arch top oblong mirror panel back, 5ft. wide. £1,100

An Edwardian George III style satinwood display cabinet banded in ebony, 48in. wide. £1,500

A mid Victorian oak and marquetry cabinet, 55in. wide, 85in. high. £2,640

A Louis Majorelle Art Nouveau walnut and rosewood virtrine, 188cm. high. £2,600

Late 18th century Dutch walnut and marquetry display cabinet, 60in. wide. £12,100

DISPLAY CABINETS

Late 19th century Japanese lacquer display cabinet, 70in. high.　　　　£3,905

Art Nouveau style oak china cabinet, 1920.　　　£75

An English Art Nouveau mahogany display cabinet with bevelled mirror back, 71in. high x 53in. wide.　　　　£980

An Edwardian mahogany china display cabinet with Gothic style astragal glazing, 4ft.6in. wide.　£520

An ormolu mounted kingwood vitrine cabinet with serpentine breccia marble top, 35in. wide.　　£1,980

A Colonial calamander display cabinet, the drawers with silver plated handles, early 19th century, 57in. wide.　　　　£1,620

A Christopher Pratt & Sons inlaid mahogany display cabinet, 192.6cm. high.　　　　£825

An Edwardian mahogany inlaid bow front corner display case with low gallery.　　　　£300

A Georgian style carved mahogany display side cabinet of serpentine outline, 4ft. 4in. wide.　£1,050

DISPLAY CABINETS

Hepplewhite mahogany china cabinet in two parts, circa 1790, 50½in. wide. £1,630

Art Nouveau style oak display cabinet.   £285

A Dutch walnut and marquetry veneered display cabinet, 46in. wide.   £2,500

A figured walnut veneered display cabinet with shaped cresting above the glazed doors, 214cm. wide. £5,940

A 19th century French mahogany and brass cabinet with brass borders and mounts, 52in. wide. £1,320

An Edwardian mahogany display cabinet crossbanded in satinwood, 57½in. wide. £1,350

Late 19th century Louis XVI style ormolu mounted marquetry vitrine, America, 38in. wide.   £2,190

An Art Nouveau mahogany display cabinet in Scottish style, with bevelled mirror top above a single leaded glass door, 54in. wide.   £650

One of a pair of ormolu mounted tulipwood display cabinets, 21¾in. wide, 57½in. high.   £5,060

DISPLAY CABINETS

A bow-fronted painted satinwood display cabinet, the cornice with a pair of urn finials, 3ft.6in. wide. £2,750

One of a pair of mid Victorian ormolu mounted satinwood side cabinets, 36in. wide. £3,080

Late Victorian mahogany china display cabinet with carved surmount, 4ft. wide. £850

A scarlet boulle and ebonised breakfront vitrine cabinet, 64in. wide. £2,420

An Edwardian satinwood display cabinet painted with flowers, ribbon-tied foliate scrolls and grisaille panels, 41in. wide. £2,400

A Victorian ebonised and brass inlaid side cabinet with glazed bow-fronted doors, 4ft.6in. wide. £480

A mahogany serpentine front standing corner cabinet with astragal glazed upper section, on ogee bracket feet, 194cm. high. £580

A Dutch walnut veneered floral marquetry inlaid cabinet, on front bun and side bracket feet, 5ft.7in. wide. £2,700

A Wylie & Lochhead mahogany display cabinet, designed by E. A. Taylor, 88cm. wide. £1,730

DISPLAY CABINETS

Gustav Stickley one door china closet, circa 1907, no. 820, 36in. wide.   £900

A mahogany display cabinet of Chinese Chippendale design enclosed by astragal glazed doors, 44in. wide.   £540

An Edwardian satinwood and marquetry china cabinet in the Sheraton taste, 1.10m. wide.   £4,000

An Edwardian inlaid mahogany display cabinet with centre serpentine shaped drawer, 50in. wide. £1,150

An Edwardian satinwood breakfront china cabinet in Sheraton revival style, 4ft.9in. wide.   £2,400

Victorian walnut and ormolu display cabinet, 1860.   £1,440

A shaped Dutch marquetry, domed top, display cabinet with brass handles, 4ft.0½in. wide.   £1,900

An Edwardian mahogany display cabinet in two parts with swan-neck pediment, blind fret carving and urn finials.   £1,250

A walnut showcase cabinet, the single door and sides with glass panels, probably Dutch, 18th/19th century, 218cm. high.   £2,815

DISPLAY CABINETS

A black and gold lacquer display cabinet with two brass mounted oval panelled glazed doors, 50½in. wide. £3,240

A 19th century Chinese hardwood display cabinet, 32in. wide. £570

A Japanese hardwood display cabinet with asymmetrical arrangement of shelves, cupboard and drawers, 4ft. 11½in. wide. £770

A figured walnut veneered display cabinet, 233cm. high. £2,970

A Dutch walnut and marquetry display cabinet with a pair of glazed doors, 59in. wide. £2,810

A Dutch walnut and marquetry display cabinet on later bun feet, 73in. wide. £4,860

An Edwardian Art Nouveau mahogany side cabinet with boxwood, satinwood and harewood stylised floral inlay, 4ft. wide. £440

Late 19th century mahogany Chinese Chippendale design display cabinet on stand, 49 x 26 x 84in. high. £3,300

A 19th century Dutch walnut veneered showcase cabinet, 225cm. high. £3,125

DRESSERS

An early 18th century oak Welsh dresser with moulded cornice, 72in. £1,800

Late 18th century George III oak dresser on ogee bracket feet, 6ft.9in. high. £4,510

An 18th century oak cupboard dresser with rack, 71½in. wide. £3,850

A Commonwealth oak and elm dresser on block feet, circa 1650, 4ft.1in. wide. £550

An 18th century oak dresser, the base with drawers and panelled cupboards with brass drop handles. £950

A George III oak and mahogany crossbanded dresser, circa 1790, 6ft.1½in. wide. £1,705

An early Georgian oak high dresser, the moulded cornice with three shelves on shaped trestle supports, 61in. wide. £6,600

An 18th century inlaid kitchen dresser with ivory escutcheons. £1,300

A late Georgian oak and fruitwood high dresser of breakfront outline, 66in. wide. £1,430

DRESSERS

Early 18th century oak dresser, 68in. wide.
£1,650

A George III oak and mahogany small dresser, circa 1780, 4ft. wide.
£2,860

A George III oak dresser raised on turned front supports, circa 1770, 6ft. 2in. wide. £1,980

A French provincial oak and chestnut dresser base on stump cabriole legs, 4ft. 4in. wide. £800

A George III oak dresser, 5ft.6in. wide, circa 1760.
£1,375

Late 18th century oak, mahogany banded dresser with rack, 72in. wide.
£1,050

Victorian oak Welsh dresser, circa 1880. £500

A George I oak and elm dresser with later carving, circa 1720, 6ft.4in. wide.
£970

An early 18th century Southern Welsh oak enclosed dresser raised on stump feet, 158cm. wide. £1,300

A George III low oak dresser with three frieze drawers, 82in. wide.   £935

An 18th century low oak dresser with a moulded top above three frieze drawers, 90 x 32in. high.   £1,870

A Georgian oak dresser, the top crossbanded with mahogany, 191cm. wide.   £1,700

A Georgian low oak dresser fitted with three frieze drawers, 80in. wide.   £1,650

An oak dresser with drawers having brass drop handles, 70in. wide.   £1,100

A George III oak dresser base raised on ogee moulded bracket supports, 212cm. wide.   £550

An 18th century crossbanded oak dresser base.   £2,500

George III oak dresser with mahogany crossbanding.   £2,200

DRESSERS

A George III oak dresser with open shelved back, circa 1790, 6ft.6in. wide. £935

A George III oak dresser, circa 1770, 5ft.4in. wide. £1,540

A mid Georgian oak dresser, the delft rack with moulded cornice, 59½in. wide. £1,900

An oak Welsh dresser on square tapering legs, 6ft. wide. £1,900

A Swiss pine dresser of architectural design, 84 x 32in. £1,000

Late 18th century oak three-drawer dresser with rack, 74in. long. £1,300

A George III oak dresser with three drawers to the base and open shelves above, 63in. wide. £1,800

Mid 18th century George II oak Welsh dresser, 58½in. long. £1,765

A George III oak break-front dresser with raised open shelf back, circa 1770, 6ft. wide. £1,925

DRESSERS

An 18th century small oak dresser, 54in. wide. £1,870

An early 19th century oak and fruitwood dresser base with three drawers, on cabriole legs, 79in. wide. £2,915

Early 18th century French walnut dresser, 4ft.7½in. wide. £4,730

An oak dresser on square cabriole legs and pad feet, mid 18th century, 78in. wide. £3,455

Early 18th century oak Welsh dresser on plank feet, 57½in. wide. £5,185

A George III oak dresser with mahogany crossbanding throughout, 85½in. wide. £1,980

A reproduction oak and mahogany crossbanded Welsh dresser, the drawers with brass loop handles, 5ft.3in. wide. £900

A Georgian oak dresser, the shelves with shaped cornice, 70½in. wide. £2,640

A Flemish-style ebonised oak dresser commemorating a 1789 wedding. £1,400

DRESSERS

Late 18th/early 19th century Welsh pine dresser, 58in. wide.   £1,375

An oak low dresser, the frieze with three fielded drawers, 71½in. wide.   £1,760

An early 18th century oak dresser, the plate rack with three shelves and two panelled doors, 85in. wide.   £1,300

Victorian pine Welsh dresser, 1860.   £330

A pine dresser with shaped back and pot board with small drawers under, 5ft. wide.   £400

Victorian pine Welsh dresser, 1840.   £445

A reproduction oak and mahogany crossbanded dresser with raised plate rack, 5ft.2in. wide.   £1,000

An early 19th century mahogany and oak dresser with brass handles, 66in. long.   £1,250

Victorian pine dresser with drawers and cupboards, 1855.   £500

DUMBWAITERS

A mid Georgian mahogany
dumbwaiter with two
turned tiers, 20in. diam.
£1,730

A Regency ormolu mounted
mahogany dumbwaiter,
26¼in. diam., 45¼in. high.
£4,950

A Regency mahogany two-
tier dumbwaiter, 36½in.
high.   £660

A George III mahogany two-
tier dumbwaiter, 20½in.
wide, 36in. high.   £5,940

A Georgian mahogany three-
tier dumbwaiter, 48in. high.
£420

A William IV mahogany
three-tier dumbwaiter,
150cm. high.   £1,400

A George III mahogany
three-tier dumbwaiter on
vase-shaped shaft, foliate
cabriole legs and pad feet,
42in. wide.   £1,836

A Regency ormolu mounted
mahogany dumbwaiter,
27in. diam., 42¾in. high.
£6,050

A George III mahogany
two-tier dumbwaiter on
tripod support, 2ft.1½in.
diam., circa 1760.   £700

HALL STANDS

An early Victorian coat stand, by John Webb, on bracket base with metal liner, 64in. wide. £1,430

Victorian mahogany hall stand, 1860. £125

A Japonnaiserie bamboo and porcelain hat and coat stand, 51in. wide, 84in. high. £1,295

Victorian oak hall stand, 1860. £140

Victorian walnut hallstand with two trays and Wedgwood tiled back, 1875. £320

Victorian walnut hall stand with two trays, 1880. £200

Victorian oak tiled back hall stand, 1860. £195

Victorian oak stickstand with brass plaque, circa 1900. £90

Victorian mahogany hall stand with two trays, 1870. £140

KNEEHOLE DESKS

A Country Federal cherry partner's desk, circa 1820, 53½in. wide.   £2,085

A George III mahogany kneehole secretaire in the manner of Gillows, with leather lined top, 49½in. wide.   £3,025

A George III mahogany partner's desk, the kneehole flanked by six graduated drawers, 55in. wide. £7,020

A Queen Anne walnut kneehole desk on bracket feet, the sides with gilt metal carrying handles, 27¾in. wide.   £11,880

An early Georgian walnut kneehole desk with brass drop handles, 75cm. wide.   £1,900

An early George III mahogany kneehole dressing table on bracket feet, 35½ x 30½in. high.   £2,255

A small mahogany kneehole secretaire desk, 29½in. wide.   £1,980

A Queen Anne walnut kneehole desk of golden colour, 32in. wide.   £11,880

A mahogany small kneehole desk in the Georgian style, 31½in. wide.   £1,265

KNEEHOLE DESKS

A George III mahogany kneehole desk with seven various
sized drawers, 33in. wide.
£1,730

A Heal's sycamore kneehole
desk, the rectangular top
with semi-circular end,
133.4cm. wide.   £440

A Queen Anne walnut knee-
hole desk on later bun feet,
36½in. wide.   £2,590

A figured walnut kneehole
desk crossbanded and inlaid
with feather-banding, basically
18th century, 32½in. wide.
£3,080

A George II mahogany kneehole desk with arched apron
and six short drawers about
a recessed enclosed cupboard,
83cm. wide.   £1,900

A George III mahogany
military dressing table, the
hinged top enclosing a fitted
interior, 36in. wide.   £1,650

An early George III maho-
gany kneehole desk with
brass handles, 33½in. wide.
£1,850

A George I walnut veneered
kneehole desk/writing chest
with herringbone line inlay,
35in. wide.   £2,100

A late Georgian small mahogany kneehole desk, 35in.
wide.   £1,430

KNEEHOLE DESKS

A George III mahogany partner's desk with leather lined top and nine drawers on both sides. 60¼in. wide. **£4,535**

A 20th century mahogany partner's desk, Steven Smith, Boston, with brass pulls and escutcheons, 58in. long. **£2,055**

A George III mahogany pedestal desk with moulded, scarlet leather lined rectangular top, 54in. wide. **£970**

A George I walnut kneehole desk on later bracket feet, 31½in. wide. **£3,520**

A Queen Anne pollard elm kneehole desk, the top crossbanded with oak herringbone bands, 33in. wide. **£3,670**

An early Georgian walnut kneehole desk with one long and eight short drawers, 32in. wide. **£3,780**

An early Georgian pollard elm kneehole desk, 37½in. wide. **£2,375**

A William and Mary figured walnut kneehole desk inlaid with feather banding, 33¾in. wide. **£4,620**

A George III mahogany kneehole dressing chest with crossbanded hinged top, 41½in. wide. **£1,980**

LINEN PRESSES

George III mahogany linen press, the panelled doors enclosing sliding trays, 4ft. x 7ft.6in. high.   £880

A Federal walnut linen press on French feet, 1800-10, 43¾in. wide.   £5,730

A Georgian mahogany linen press fitted with brass ring handles, 93in. high. £1,600

A Federal mahogany linen press, in two sections, New York, 1800-15, 46¼in. wide.   £3,055

A Queen Anne burr walnut press cupboard, 5ft. wide, circa 1710.   £8,250

A Federal mahogany linen press, signed by I. Bailey, New Jersey, 1807, 48in. wide.   £5,730

Late 18th century George III inlaid mahogany linen press on bracket feet, 47½in. wide.   £3,230

A Chippendale mahogany and mahogany veneer linen press, circa 1780, 48in. wide.   £11,110

A Federal inlaid mahogany linen press, in two sections, probably New York, circa 1785-1805, 45in. wide.   £4,200

LOWBOYS

A Chippendale style carved walnut dressing table on acanthus carved cabriole legs, 36in. wide. £1,525

George I oak lowboy. £780

A George II mahogany rectangular lowboy, the drawers with wooden handles, 32in. wide. £2,500

A Queen Anne maple dressing table on four cabriole legs ending in pad feet, circa 1760, 33in. wide. £6,420

A Queen Anne maple dressing table with one long and three short drawers, 31¾in. wide. £1,125

An early Georgian walnut lowboy with three drawers above the waved apron, 32in. wide. £1,405

A walnut lowboy, the shaped frieze with three drawers on shell and husk cabriole legs, 30½in. wide. £45,000

A Dutch burr walnut lowboy with moulded waved top, early 18th century, 30in. wide. £3,240

A Queen Anne walnut dressing table on tapering cylindrical legs with disc feet, 33in. wide, 1735-50. £6,110

LOWBOYS

An early George III mahogany lowboy on cabriole legs and pad feet, 32in. wide. **£3,960**

An early 18th century gilt and gesso japanned side table on cabriole legs, 82cm. wide. **£9,000**

An 18th century Scottish red walnut lowboy with carved and scrolled kneehole, 33½in. wide. **£1,950**

An early Georgian walnut side table with arched and waved frieze, 29in. wide. **£4,320**

Early 18th century walnut lowboy, 29½in. wide. **£1,500**

A burr walnut lowboy, featherbanded in ash with quarter veneered moulded top, 33½in. wide, basically late 17th century. **£1,500**

An early Georgian oak side table, the frieze with three drawers on lappeted club legs and pad feet, 34in. wide. **£1,210**

An early Georgian oak lowboy on cabriole legs and trifid feet, 31¼in. wide. **£990**

A 19th century Dutch walnut and foliate marquetry lowboy, 27in. wide. **£1,000**

MUSIC STANDS

A Regency rosewood duet music stand, the pierced top filled with lyres. **£700**

A mid Victorian walnut music stand, the slope on an adjustable brass shaft, 23in. wide. **£660**

A Regency rosewood double-sided music stand, the sides with candle sconces, 48in. high. **£2,200**

A mid Victorian black and mother-of-pearl japanned papier mache music stand, 17¾in. diam. **£430**

An Emile Galle walnut and marquetry music stand, 90.4cm. high when not extended. **£970**

A mid Victorian black, gilt and mother-of-pearl japanned papier mache music stand, 50¼in. high. **£540**

A Regency mahogany adjustable music stand with fitted candleslides, 18in. high. **£900**

A Regency brass music stand with blue painted and gilded rest pierced with oak leaves and acorns, 60½in. high. **£1,190**

Unusual Victorian music stand with papier mache top inlaid with mother-of-pearl, circa 1850. **£660**

SCREENS

Victorian bamboo fire-
screen, 1880.   £40

Regency rosewood pole
screen, circa 1830.   £170

Chinese two-fold inlaid
screen, 1860.   £255

Victorian mahogany three-
fold screen, 1880.   £145

Late 18th century coromandel
twelve-fold screen, China, 99½in.
high, panel width 19½in.   £12,500

One of a pair of Regency
parcel gilt and cream painted
firescreens with later glazed
adjustable panels, 18in. wide.
£390

A giltwood three-leaf screen
with arched panels applied
with silk and painted with
paeonies and foliage, each
leaf 59 x 22½in.   £2,860

A mahogany polescreen with
rectangular petit point
needlework panel worked
with the parable of the Pro-
digal Son, 60in. high. £3,670

An ebonised and marquetry
four-leaf screen inlaid in
satinwood, beechwood, walnut and stained fruitwood,
190cm. high, 141cm. wide.
£1,540

SCREENS

A Dutch painted leather six-leaf screen, late 18th century, each leaf 95½ x 21½in. £1,430

An early Victorian rosewood firescreen with glazed panel, 40in. wide, 63in. high. £540

A painted leather four-leaf screen, each leaf 66 x 19½in. £1,320

An Empire mahogany cheval firescreen, the screen filled with distressed silk, 24in. wide. £305

Late 19th century fundame two-leaf table screen inlaid in Shibayama style, signed Nobuyuki, each leaf 25 x 14cm. £1,980

An Arts & Crafts oak firescreen, the framework enclosing a panel of Morris & Co. fabric woven with 'The Tulip and Rose', 55.5cm. high. £190

A Regency mahogany four-leaf screen, the divided panels with Chinese wallpaper, slightly distressed, each leaf 78 x 21½in. £8,100

A painted Japanese two-part folding screen, gouache and silver leaf, circa 1860, 55 x 49½in. £2,375

A Dutch painted leather four-leaf screen decorated with parrots and exotic birds, each leaf 84¼ x 20in. £880

136

SCREENS

An 18th century Dutch polychrome painted leather six-leaf screen, each leaf 22in. wide, 84in. high. £20,900

A Chippendale mahogany polescreen, Mass., 1765-85, 58in. high.　£3,230

A Regency black and gold lacquer six-leaf screen, each leaf 108 x 23¾in.　£6,820

A mid Victorian black, gilt and mother-of-pearl japanned firescreen, 52in. high. £1,870

A four-leaf screen decorated with 18th century Chinese wallpaper, each leaf 86 x 21½in.　£3,780

A silk-embroidered firescreen, attributed to Morris & Co., 97.5cm. high.　£220

A 19th century spinach-green jade and hardwood four-leaf screen, each leaf 211 x 43cm.　£9,350

Early 19th century Dutch painted four-leaf screen, one panel distressed, each panel 72 x 21in.　£1,730

An Indian hardwood three-leaf screen, each leaf 76 x 32in.　£505

SCREENS

A Chinese Export black and gold lacquer eight-leaf screen depicting the history of tea-making, 18th century, each leaf 84 x 21½in. £20,520

One of a pair of George III mahogany polescreens, the adjustable panels with later silk floral sprays, 14½in. wide. £325

A late 18th/early 19th century Chinese painted six-leaf screen decorated in colours with an extensive view, each leaf 23½in. wide, 83in. high. £14,040

Late 19th century ivory mounted two-leaf table screen, signed Shizan (for the Shibayama inlay) and Shinko (for the lacquer decoration). £2,375

An eight-fold gold-ground coromandel screen decorated in polychrome, each fold 7ft. high, 1ft.4in. wide. £1,100

A six-leaf Japanese screen, sumi and colour on gold paper, signed, 26 x 80in. each leaf. £2,250

An 18th century Chinese Export black and gold lacquer eight-leaf screen, each leaf 22in. wide, 76½in. high. £6,480

One of a pair of Regency giltwood screens, with glazed Beauvais tapestry panels, 24½in. wide. £970

Late 19th century ivory mounted two-leaf lacquer table screen decorated in Shibayama style, signed Masayuki, each panel 30 x 16.5cm. £1,510

SCREENS

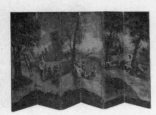

An 18th century Dutch six-leaf canvas screen painted with rustic scenes, each leaf 21¼in. wide, 65¼in. high. £3,240

One of a pair of William IV rosewood polescreens, the brass shafts with faded crimson silk banners, 19in. wide. £650

An 18th century Chinese black and gold lacquer eight-leaf screen, each leaf 81in. high, 21in. wide. £23,760

An 18th century coromandel lacquer eight-leaf screen incised and decorated in colours, each leaf 15¾in. wide, 83in. high. £4,860

A Victorian mahogany polescreen with oval framed adjustable screen, circa 1870. £260

A Japanese Export lacquer and Shibayama inlaid two-fold screen, decorated in bone, mother-of-pearl, ivory and hardwood, each fold 2ft.5½in. wide, 5ft.7in. high. £610

An 18th century Dutch painted and gilded leather six-leaf screen, each leaf 108in. high, 21in. wide. £3,890

A Charles X fruitwood and ebonised firescreen with glazed needlework panel, 53½in. high. £1,510

A late 19th century four-fold low screen in maroon velvet and bands of Berlin woolwork, 41in. high, each fold 18in. £2,375

SECRETAIRE BOOKCASES

A George III mahogany secretaire bookcase, circa 1790, 3ft.4in. wide.
£3,410

A George III mahogany secretaire bookcase with two thirteen pane glazed doors, 44in. wide.
£1,870

A Chippendale carved maple desk and bookcase, Rhode Island, 1750-80, 82in. high, 38in. wide. £17,420

Mid 18th century George III mahogany butler's secretary desk in two sections, 46in. wide.
£4,310

A Georgian carved mahogany secretaire breakfront library bookcase in the Chippendale taste, 2.20m. wide. £8,000

A George III mahogany secretaire cabinet with a pair of glazed cupboard doors, 46½in. wide. £2,310

A George III mahogany secretaire cabinet with two glazed doors, 49in. wide.
£3,240

A mahogany secretaire bookcase with four glazed doors enclosing adjustable shelves, 55in. wide.
£1,600

A Federal mahogany and mahogany veneer inlaid secretary, Mass., circa 1815, 39in. wide. £3,085

SECRETAIRE BOOKCASES

A Regency mahogany secretaire cabinet, the doors flanked by ebony mouldings, 49in. wide. £4,860

A Federal mahogany inlaid desk/bookcase, probably Mass., circa 1800, 37½in. wide. £2,310

A Regency mahogany secretaire cabinet with a pair of gothic pattern glazed doors, 43in. wide. £1,980

A George III mahogany secretaire cabinet with a pair of glazed cupboard doors, 45½in. wide. £2,590

A Federal inlaid mahogany breakfront secretary bookcase, Salem, Mass., 1795-1800, 67in. wide. £181,445

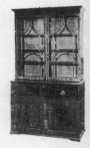

A 19th century secretaire bookcase with a stepped cornice, dated 1792, 47in. wide. £2,800

A George III mahogany secretaire cabinet with a pair of glazed cupboard doors, 43½in. wide. £4,320

A George III satinwood and rosewood secretaire cabinet, the baize-lined fall-flap enclosing a fitted interior, 36in. wide. £9,720

A George III satinwood secretaire bookcase with circular enamelled ring handles, 30¾in. wide. £46,200

SECRETAIRE BOOKCASES

An Empire stencilled mahogany secretary in two parts,
New York, 1820-30, 42¼in.
wide.   £5,460

A Federal mahogany secre-
tary bookcase, in two parts,
circa 1805/25, 39½in. wide.
                          £2,275

A George III mahogany
secretaire cabinet, 49½in.
wide.   £8,800

A George III mahogany
secretaire cabinet, the
secretaire drawer with fruitwood and maple veneers,
43½in. wide.   £2,915

An Edwardian mahogany
secretaire bookcase in the
Sheraton revival manner,
240 x 127cm.   £1,600

A George III satinwood
secretaire cabinet with
geometrically-glazed doors,
31½in. wide.   £20,520

A Regency mahogany secre-
taire cabinet with two gothic
pattern glazed cupboard
doors, 43in. wide.   £3,595

George III mahogany secretaire
bookcase, circa 1810, 44in.
wide.   £720

A Regency mahogany
secretaire bookcase, the
base with fall-front fitted
writing drawer, 47½in. wide.
                          £4,400

SECRETAIRE BOOKCASES

A George III mahogany
secretaire cabinet with a pair
of gothic glazed doors
enclosing later shelves, 44in.
wide.   £3,300

An English 19th century
Chippendale style maho-
gany secretaire cabinet,
86in. long.   £15,275

A George III mahogany and
burr yew secretaire cabinet,
41½in. wide.   £9,900

A George III mahogany
secretaire cabinet with
moulded tear-drop cor-
nice, 49in. wide.   £3,670

A Federal mahogany secre-
tary with glazed panel doors
above a fold-down writing
surface, circa 1795, 40in.
wide.   £5,280

A satinwood secretaire bookcase, late 18th century,
possibly Anglo-Indian, 31½in.
wide.   £4,105

A George III mahogany
secretaire bookcase with a
pair of gothic glazed doors,
46in. wide.   £2,090

A Regency yewwood and
laburnum crossbanded
secretaire bookcase, 1.74m.
high, 95cm. wide.   £3,600

A George III mahogany
secretaire bookcase with
original brass swan neck
handles, 3ft.8in. wide.
                     £3,200

FURNITURE

SECRETAIRES

Late 18th/early 19th century gilt metal mounted mahogany secretaire a abattant, 37½in. wide.
£1,620

Late 18th century floral marquetry secretary, Holland, 48in. wide.
£1,710

A late George III mahogany secretaire cabinet, the doors enclosing sliding tray shelves, 46in. wide.
£1,320

A Regency rosewood secretaire cabinet, the baize-lined drawer with fitted interior, 23in. wide.
£11,340

A late George III mahogany and partridgewood secretaire, 30½in. wide.
£1,405

A late George II mahogany writing cabinet, 3ft.4½in. wide, circa 1760.
£13,200

A Renaissance Revival walnut butler's secretary, circa 1860, 40¾in. wide.
£1,225

A Federal inlaid mahogany bureau desk, possibly by M. Allison, 1790/1810, N.Y., 46½in. wide.
£3,035

A Georgian mahogany secretaire press. £850

SECRETAIRES

A George III cedar secretaire bookcase, 47in. wide. £1,080

A Louis XVI kingwood and tulipwood semainier by J. J. Kirschenbach, 56in. high. £3,240

A walnut and yewwood secretaire cabinet, 41½in. wide. £2,200

A Queen Anne walnut secretaire with a moulded cornice above a cushion frieze drawer, 40½in. wide. £3,300

A George III mahogany secretaire press with Gothic cornice and fitted trays to upper section, 48in. wide. £2,400

A Louis Phillipe kingwood veneered small secretaire a abattant with a marble top, 26in. wide. £900

An ormolu mounted, parquetry and marquetry secretaire a abattant of Louis XVI style, on toupie feet, 30in. wide. £1,650

A Federal mahogany tambour secretary, circa 1795, 40in. wide. £3,055

A George I walnut secretaire cabinet, the upper part with eight drawers and adjustable shelves, 47in. wide. £3,400

SECRETAIRES

An early Georgian walnut secretaire, the convex frieze drawer and fall-flap inlaid with chevron lines, 43½in. wide.   £2,160

A George III mahogany secretaire chest, the writing drawer enclosing a fitted interior, circa 1770, 2ft. 10in. wide.   £900

A George III mahogany secretaire cabinet, 30in. wide, 63½in. high.   £7,560

A 16th century Spanish vargueno, the interior has seventeen ivory and gilt moulded drawers, 38in. long.   £1,695

A Chinese side cabinet with fitted drawer and cupboard above.   £1,000

A Louis XVI tulipwood and chequer inlaid secretaire a abattant with later gilt metal ornament, 97cm. wide.   £1,300

A George III mahogany and kingwood crossbanded secretaire cabinet, circa 1790, 3ft.1in. wide.   £3,300

Gustav Stickley oak and wrought iron secretary, designed by Harvey Ellis, circa 1904, 56in. wide.   £9,090

Late Empire figured mahogany secretary on scroll feet, circa 1835, 46¼in. wide.   £660

SECRETAIRES

A George III mahogany
secretaire on ogee bracket
feet, 32½in. wide.
£32,400

A pale mahogany Campaign
chest with central secretaire
drawer.   £1,000

A George III mahogany
secretaire cabinet on fluted
square legs and block feet,
43in. wide.   £81,000

A mid 18th century Con-
tinental inlaid secretaire
chest of various woods,
40½in. wide.   £950

A George III satinwood
secretaire, with fitted secretaire drawer above two long
and one deep drawer, 32½in.
wide.   £5,940

Late 19th century marque-
try secretaire with pull-out
secretary drawer, Holland,
41½in. wide.   £875

A 19th century German
(Ludwig II) ormolu moun-
ted Japanese black and
gold lacquer cartonnier,
46½in. wide.   £20,520

A Chippendale mahogany
bureau with four drawers,
Boston, circa 1790, 36½in.
wide.   £12,500

An 18th century walnut
secretaire a abattant with
fall front, 36in. wide.
£3,000

SETTEES & COUCHES

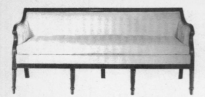

A Federal upholstered mahogany sofa on ring turned and reeded legs, circa 1800-15, 75½in. long. £3,435

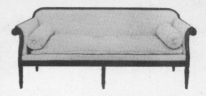

Late 18th century carved fruitwood settee, 82in. long. £560

A Victorian chaise longue with carved mahogany show wood frame and cabriole legs and gold damask cover. £580

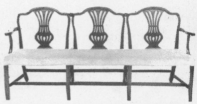

Late 18th/early 19th century George III walnut three-back settee, England, 76¾in. wide. £1,310

One of a pair of Regency rosewood sofas with triple cushion backs and cushion seats covered in green velvet, 77in. wide. £12,960

A mid Georgian oak and mahogany cross-banded settle on cabriole supports and pad feet, 72in. wide. £345

A mahogany daybed upholstered in blue moire, 65in. long, the castors and leg stamped Howard & Sons Ltd., London. £825

Stripped pine bench, circa 1900. £300

SETTEES & COUCHES

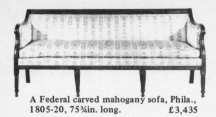

A Federal carved mahogany sofa, Phila.,
1805-20, 75¾in. long.   £3,435

One of a pair of grain painted 'fancy' settees,
each with a back of four sections, 74in. wide,
1800-10.   £3,435

A Biedermeier satin-birch sofa with padded
rectangular box back, 72in. wide.   £1,430

A Federal mahogany sofa, the upholstered
back and seat with beaded bow front, probably Mass., circa 1810, 73in. wide.
                                          £2,500

A Federal mahogany sofa, the padded back
with arched crest, 1790-1810, 80¼in. wide.
                                          £3,055

A George III mahogany humpback sofa
with plum-coloured floral damask loose
cover, squab and four cushions, 85in.
wide.   £5,400

A giltwood daybed in the Theban style, 79½in.
wide.   £13,200

An early George II mahogany sofa in
the French taste, the serpentine seat
covered in green silk repp, 61in. wide.
                                          £3,240

SETTEES & COUCHES

A Victorian carved walnut and upholstered double chair-back settee, 5ft.9in. wide.
£1,320

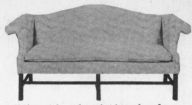

A Chippendale style stained maple sofa on moulded Marlborough legs, 76in. long.
£1,865

Part of a carved mahogany bergere lounge suite of five pieces, the settee with three-panel back and padded seat.
£1,400

An L. & J. G. Stickley slat-back settle, style no. 281, with spring cushion seat, circa 1912, 76in. wide.
£1,110

A Federal carved mahogany sofa, attributed to the shop of Duncan Phyfe, N.Y., 1800-20, 80in. wide.
£32,660

A Victorian walnut chaise longue with buttoned graduated back panel, 83in. long.
£1,300

A walnut sofa with padded back and seat, with outscrolled arm supports, on shell and husk cabriole legs and pad feet, 62in. wide.
£3,455

A small, George III, mahogany humpback sofa with upholstered back, scrolled arms and waved seat on square tapering legs, 63in. wide.
£6,265

SETTEES & COUCHES

A George III mahogany sofa with serpentine back, Irish, late 18th century, 86in. wide.
£2,290

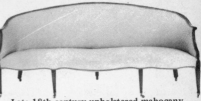

Late 18th century upholstered mahogany Sheraton sofa, 79in. long. £1,500

A 'Lip' sofa after a design by Salvador Dali, upholstered in red nylon stretch fabric, 209cm. wide. £1,510

Late 19th century rococo Revival rosewood settee, N. Schott, America, 65in. wide.
£650

A George IV brass inlaid mahogany and rosewood chaise longue with scrolling padded back, sides and foot rest, 82in. wide.
£1,190

A Chippendale upholstered sofa, the serpentine back flanked by outward flaring arms, circa 1780, 80in. long. £2,360

A Regency simulated bamboo sofa with pierced triple chairback, cane filled seat and squab cushion, 54in. wide. £1,620

A Louis XVI giltwood canape with curved and arched padded back and bowed seat covered in floral gros point needlework, 93in. wide. £3,025

SETTEES & COUCHES

William IV rosewood chaise with scroll carved arm and back rail, lotus carved foot, 86in. long. £580

'Anfibio', a white leather upholstered sofa bed designed by Alessandro Becchi, 240cm. wide. £595

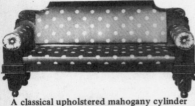

A classical upholstered mahogany cylinder arm sofa, circa 1810-30, 72in. long. £685

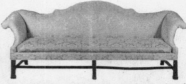

A Chippendale mahogany serpentine-back sofa on Marlborough legs with blocked feet joined by stretchers, Phila., 1765-85, 109½in. wide. £423,380

A George I walnut and beechwood settee covered in petit and gros point floral needlework, 64in. wide. £41,800

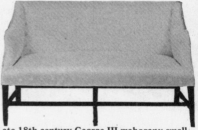

Late 18th century George III mahogany small sofa on square tapering legs, on brass cuffs, 50in. wide. £2,295

A George III mahogany sofa upholstered in apricot silk, 66in. wide. £2,160

A George III giltwood small sofa in the manner of Thos. Chippendale, the back and seat covered in blue and white floral printed cotton, 58in. wide. £2,160

SETTEES & COUCHES

A William IV giltwood chaise longue with scrolled upholstered back, seat and footrest, 92in. wide. £1,025

One of a pair of George II mahogany twin chairback settees, with arms ending in eagles' masks, 64in. wide. £19,440

Late 18th century Louis XVI painted canape, repainted white and gilt, probably Sweden, 86in. long. £450

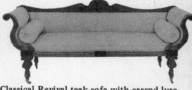

Classical Revival teak sofa with carved lyre legs terminating in turned feet with brass cap castors, China, circa 1840, 86in. long. £1,400

A Louis XVI white painted banquette with rectangular back, bowed seat and squab covered in blue floral chintz, 53in. wide. £1,045

A George III mahogany sofa, the arched padded back, out-scrolled arms and bowed seat on moulded square legs, 77in. wide. £4,535

An ebonised sofa with rectangular back, sides and seat covered in a floral brocade with wild animals, 60in. wide. £1,045

A George III mahogany frame settee with a stuff over back and seat. £1,100

SHELVES & BRACKETS

A George III hanging shelf with chinoiserie and Gothic fretwork back and sides, 26¼in. wide. £1,613

Victorian mahogany hanging hat rack, 1900. £60

One of a pair of late George III carved mahogany hanging shelves, 35½in. wide. £8,066

Gustav Stickley inlaid tiger maple open music stand, circa 1904, no. 670, signed with Eastwood label, 39in. high. £5,069

Victorian mahogany three-tier dinner wagon, 1870. £300

A yewwood writing and shelf unit with open shelves above two glazed doors, 28in. wide. £1,100

A set of George III pierced fret side mahogany wall shelves, 19in. wide. £540

Barley twist oak trolley with tray, 1900. £40

L. & J. G. Stickley open magazine rack, circa 1910, 42in. high, 21in. wide. £769

FURTURE

SHELVES & BRACKETS

Victorian oak hanging cabinet, 1880. £62

Roycroft oak magazine pedestal, East Aurora, N.Y., circa 1910, 48in. high. £530

A James I set of three open shelves, circa 1620, 3ft.10½in. wide. £8,580

A Louis XV-style kingwood and floral marquetry two-tier etagere, 2ft.7½in. wide, circa 1900. £570

An early 19th century mahogany adjustable map reading/ buffet stand, 3ft. £420

Gustav Stickley open slat-sided bookshelf, circa 1909, 27in. wide. £560

A Regency simulated rosewood hanging open bookshelf, 57cm. wide, 75cm. high. £1,900

An Isokon book stand, white painted natural wood, with sloping book compartments, 40.3cm. high. £216

Victorian oak bookstand, 1880. £65

SIDEBOARDS

A Federal inlaid mahogany serpentine front sideboard, circa 1780/1800, 74½in. wide. £6,450

Federal mahogany inlaid sideboard, New England, circa 1790, 51in. wide. £2,200

A Federal mahogany sideboard, the top with broad ovolo corners, circa 1795, 69in. wide. £5,035

A Federal mahogany sideboard with serpentine top, Maryland, 1790-1810, 72in. wide. £7,640

A Regency mahogany sideboard, inlaid with bands of brass ovals on an ebonised ground, 88½in. wide. £12,960

A Sheraton period mahogany sideboard inlaid with satinwood and ebony herringbone stringing, 68in. wide. £1,350

A Victorian rococo style flame mahogany pedestal sideboard with two central serpentine drawers, 7ft. wide. £650

A Federal mahogany veneer sideboard with bowed rectangular top, 1790-1815, 70in. wide. £3,055

SIDEBOARDS

A George III mahogany secretaire sideboard, with central fitted secretaire drawer , 5ft.1in. wide, circa 1790. £2,145

A classical mahogany sideboard with marble top, New York, 1815-25, 75in. long. £2,290

A George III mahogany and satinwood sideboard with crossbanded D-shaped top, 48in. wide. £7,020

A Federal mahogany sideboard, the top with bowed front edge, circa 1795/1815, 75½in. wide. £2,730

A George III mahogany sideboard with bowed concave centred top, the drawer crossbanded with rosewood in the arched centre, 72in. wide. £10,260

A Federal mahogany inlaid sideboard with bow front, Mass., circa 1815, 70in. wide. £6,080

A Federal mahogany sideboard, the front with a pair of cockbeaded short drawers centred by a bowed long drawer, 69½in. long, circa 1785-1800. £3,435

A mahogany Sheraton-style sideboard with crossbanded decoration , 66in. long. £1,700

SIDEBOARDS

A Federal mahogany sideboard, the top shaped to fit a curved recess, circa 1790, 73in. wide. £4,965

A George III mahogany apsidal sideboard inlaid with satinwood strung borders, 3ft. high by 5ft.5½in. wide, circa 1790. £825

A late Georgian mahogany sweep front sideboard on six turned supports, 54¼in. wide. £1,540

Georgian mahogany four-door sideboard, 1840. £955

Late Georgian figured mahogany breakfront sideboard with lion mask ring handles, 5ft.7in. wide. £725

A Federal mahogany sideboard with D-shaped top, Rhode Island, 1790-1810, 67in. long. £5,345

A Regency mahogany sideboard with ebony stringing and bowed top, 69½in. wide. £3,455

A Regency mahogany sideboard with breakfront D-shaped crossbanded top, 63½in. wide. £1,320

SIDEBOARDS

A George III mahogany serpentine sideboard with a central drawer above an arch, flanked by deep drawers, 67in. wide. £7,700

A George III mahogany and satinwood bow fronted sideboard with a cellarette drawer to the right and a cupboard to the left, 72in. wide. £3,890

A George III mahogany and satinwood sideboard with gilt metal and enamel handles, Scottish, 103in. wide. £9,180

A Sheraton mahogany inlaid breakfront sideboard with cellarette drawer and cupboard, 82in. wide. £1,500

A George III mahogany sideboard with serpentine top, with one frieze drawer, flanked by two deep drawers, one a cellarette drawer, 79in. wide. £1,945

A George III mahogany breakfront sideboard with brass drop handles, 153cm. wide. £1,150

A Federal inlaid carved mahogany sideboard with serpentine top, attributed to Ephraim Haines, Phila., 1800-15. £6,545

A George III mahogany sideboard with crossbanded serpentine top, 65½in. wide. £5,940

SIDEBOARDS

A 19th century mahogany sideboard, the bow fronted top inlaid with a broad satinwood band and two floral and foliate roundels, 6ft. wide.
£2,300

A Federal inlaid mahogany sideboard, with serpentine-shaped top, 1790-1815, 73½in. wide.
£3,850

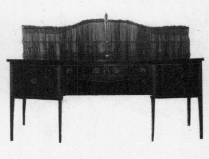

A George III mahogany sideboard with four short and two cellarette drawers, 46in. wide.
£990

A Sheraton period bowfronted mahogany sideboard, the top with brass rail and rosewood edge bands, 7ft. wide.
£2,300

Gustav Stickley eight-legged sideboard, circa 1904, no. 817, with plate rack, 70in. wide.
£4,895

A Regency mahogany breakfront sideboard, inlaid with ebonised lines, the top with a later superstructure with four tambour shutters, possibly Scottish, 84in. wide.
£1,295

SIDEBOARDS

A late George III mahogany bowfront sideboard on ring turned tapering legs and feet, 72½in. long. £1,320

A George III mahogany sideboard with serpentine crossbanded top, the double-arched centre with a drawer flanked by two deep drawers, 72in. wide. £17,600

A mahogany sideboard with serpentine top and ledge back, 56½in. wide. £3,850

A Regency mahogany breakfront sideboard inlaid with ebonised lines, 84½in. wide. £1,540

George III inlaid mahogany sideboard, the bowfronted top with satinwood crossbanding, 52in. wide. £1,680

A Sheraton period mahogany veneered bowfronted sideboard with satinwood line inlay and stringing, 4ft.9in. wide. £4,100

STANDS

Victorian mahogany and brass cakestand, 1875. £60

A George III green painted and gilded jardiniere after a design by Robert Adam, 36in. wide. £37,800

Victorian walnut pedestal, 1860. £250

A Gustav Stickley three-drawer bedside stand, style no. 842, copper hardware with loop handles, circa 1907, 29½in. high. £765

One of a pair of George III gilt-wood torcheres on cloven hoof feet, 49½in. high. £12,960

Victorian oak three-tiered buffet, circa 1870. £125

A William and Mary walnut torchere with moulded circular top, spirally-turned shaft and scrolled tripartite base, 12in. diam. £595

An early 18th century Italian carved giltwood stand with a simulated green marble top, 1.10m. high. £800

A Thonet stained beechwood plant stand, the design attributed to Josef Hoffmann, 119cm. high. £605

STANDS

A George II grained pine pedestal, 53¼in. high.
£7,150

Victorian pine and cast iron butter maker, 1860. £215

Victorian oak barley twist cakestand, 1860. £40

A Regency mahogany three-tier etagere, the grey marble shelves with ormolu galleries, 24½in. wide. £9,720

One of a pair of George II mahogany torcheres, 3ft. 4in. high, 11in. diam., circa 1755. £2,970

A William and Mary walnut stand, Penn., 1700-40, 25¼in. wide. £1,365

One of a pair of William and Mary walnut and marquetry torcheres, 10¾in. diam., 35½in. high. £2,590

An elephant's foot waste-paper basket with rosewood rim and ivory plaque, 11in. high. £495

A carved mahogany galleried kettle stand, the top with open baluster gallery, 30cm. diam., 75cm. high. £1,600

An ormolu mounted mahogany gueridon in the manner of Weisweiler, 30½in. high.   £3,890

A Federal inlaid mahogany corner stand, the top with a pierced brass gallery, probably New York, 1800-15, 34½in. high.   £1,890

A mid 19th century French bronze tripod with inset circular green marble top, 34½in. high.   £3,300

An early Victorian walnut folio stand with pierced adjustable twin-flap top, 28in. wide.   £3,300

A Gufram hat-stand, designed by Guido Drocco and Franco Mello, modelled as a cactus plant, 1971, 174.5cm. high.   £2,810

Late 19th century Eastlake folio stand.   £720

Victorian mahogany shaving stand, 1880.   £195

A George IV mahogany library bookstand with a panelled fall-flap, 45½in. wide.   £755

A polished chromium hat stand made for Bazzi in Milan, 51.6cm. high.   £453

STANDS

Victorian brass bound oak jardiniere, circa 1880. £55

Painted Tramp art stand with drawers, possibly New York, 1820-40, 17½in. wide. £200

One of a pair of giltwood stands with stepped circular white marble tops, 19in. wide. £3,240

A Victorian mahogany folio stand with brass ratcheted adjustable open slatted slopes, 76cm. high. £1,700

A painted and parcel gilt Blackamoor torchere, carved as a negress, 62½in. high. £1,650

A Regency mahogany reading stand, the sloping writing surface lined with tooled green leather, 23½in. wide. £15,120

French marble and ormolu pedestal, 1860. £300

An early Victorian walnut coal bin of sarcophagus form with coffered top and hinged front with metal liner, 21in. wide. £1,080

A pine easel, adjustable, on a trestle base, with castors, 29in. wide. £495

STANDS

A spinning wheel with bobbin turned spokes. £165

Limbert round tall pedestal, circa 1906, no. 267, 32½in. high, 14in. diam. £630

A Regency mahogany reading stand with adjustable top, 30½in. wide. £860

Victorian inlaid mahogany towel rail, circa 1880. £70

Victorian mahogany butler's tray with stand, 1860. £155

One of a pair of ormolu mounted cloisonne etageres, each with two rectangular tiers, 20¼in. wide. £3,890

One of a pair of classical Revival carved and gilt pedestals with marble tops, circa 1835, 36½in. high. £3,195

A pair of parcel gilt and painted Blackamoors of a negro and negress, 76¼in. high. £4,950

A Regency burr walnut and giltwood torchere with concave-sided triangular top, 17in. wide. £3,455

STANDS

A Federal inlaid mahogany corner stand, New York, 1790-1810, 23in. wide. £5,660

Victorian mahogany tiled top plant stand, 1860. £80

Victorian oak double-shelf cakestand, 1880. £70

One of two Regency rosewood tripod jardinieres, one bearing the label of Richard Henry Masters, possibly Anglo-Indian, 34½in. high. £4,860

One of a pair of mid Victorian oak and ebonised umbrella stands in the Gothic taste, 66in. wide. £660

A Japanese carved padouk-wood urn stand with circular inset marble top, 10in. diam. £170

One of a pair of walnut torcheres with lobed tray-tops and hexagonal shaped shafts, 10in. wide, 30½in. high. £755

A pair of late 18th century Italian parcel gilt and green painted torcheres, 69½in. high. £5,500

An ormolu mounted amboyna gueridon in the manner of Weisweiler, the top with turquoise ground saucer inscribed Sevres RF Sc, 30in. high. £2,270

FURNITURE

A set of late George III mahogany bedside steps, circa 1820, 2ft.6in. high. £1,760

A Regency mahogany metamorphic library chair/steps in the manner of Morgan & Saunders, circa 1820. £1,760

An American inlaid mahogany and cherrywood bed step, 1790-1820, 21in. high. £660

An early 19th century metamorphic set of mahogany folding library steps, 36in. high extended. £560

A set of late George III mahogany bedside steps, circa 1800, 1ft.11in. high. £2,200

A George III mahogany library steps table with moulded hinged top, 48in. high, extended. £2,160

One of a pair of Regency mahogany metamorphic library armchairs, the seat opening to reveal four treads, 23in. wide. £12,960

An inlaid mahogany step commode with liner, 26½ x 17in. high. £120

One of a set of George III mahogany library steps, with carrying handles, 30in. wide. £2,810

STOOLS

A cream painted and parcel gilt stool, the oval seat upholstered in a pale blue and white cotton, 33½in. wide. £2,200

One of a pair of mid 19th century giltwood tabourets, covered in pink silk with gold stencilled dots, 21in. diam. £2,090

A Georgian rosewood stool with a floral tapestry covered seat, 22½in. wide. £750

A Hepplewhite period stool, with upholstered serpentine seat, on mahogany legs. £310

Late 17th century oak coffin stool, initialled WC, 18½in. wide. £1,430

An early Victorian stool on cabriole legs, 26in. wide. £290

A mid 16th century Tuscan carved walnut prie dieu, 2ft. 3in. wide. £1,540

Late 19th century pottery garden seat, probably France, whimsically depicting a cushion resting on a basket, 20in. high. £530

A 17th century oak oblong stool on baluster supports, 1ft.6in. wide. £180

Gustav Stickley spindle-sided footstool, circa 1907, no. 395, 15in. high. **£105**

A walnut stool, the drop-in seat with gros and petit point needlework, 22in. wide. **£540**

A George III-style window seat of Chippendale design, upholstered in hide with brass studding. **£420**

A George III mahogany window seat, the seat and arms upholstered in pale pink floral damask, 30in. wide. **£660**

A Spanish brass and wrought-iron faldistorio, partly 17th century. **£2,420**

A Derby & Co. oak window seat, the cut-out armrests with spindle supports, circa 1910, 28in. high. **£260**

A Dutch 18th century style mahogany marquetry stool on claw and ball feet, 21in. wide. **£440**

One of a pair of oak stools, each with a squab, Italian or Spanish, 23½in. wide. **£660**

One of a pair of mahogany stools, the seats with petit point needlework sprays on a camel-coloured ground, the cabriole legs carved with clasps and claw-and-ball feet. **£3,850**

STOOLS

One of a pair of George I needlework covered walnut stools, 1ft.7½in. wide, circa 1715.   £20,900

A George II walnut and parcel gilt stool on cabriole legs, 24½in. wide.   £10,450

A Queen Anne walnut stool, the rectangular seat covered in floral tapestry woven with a fable, 18¾in. wide. £4,105

A Biedermeier mahogany tabouret with padded seat, stamped G. Jacob with a fleur-de-lys, 24in. wide.   £1,430

An Elizabethan joint stool, circa 1580, made of inlaid padoukwood.   £4,000

A Regency parcel gilt and simulated rosewood X-framed stool, the seat with a squab cushion covered in striped silk, 35in. wide.   £2,200

A walnut and parcel gilt stool of George I style, the drop-in seat painted in gilt and scarlet with a coat-of-arms, 26in. wide. £2,160

Late 17th/early 18th century oak and elm joint stool, 18½in. wide.   £1,730

A George I walnut stool with rectangular needlework drop-in seat, on shell and foliate cabriole legs, 22in. wide.   £2,160

STOOLS

A George II mahogany foot-stool, the upholstered seat on cabriole legs, 22in. wide. £860

A Federal carved mahogany window seat, attributed to the shop of Duncan Phyfe, N.Y., 1810-20, 40in. wide. £17,420

A George I red walnut stool with a slip-in seat and shaped apron, on cabriole legs. £3,400

A Jacobean oak stool with rising top. £880

A Napoleon III giltwood stool, designed by A. M. E. Fournier, 29½in. diam. £2,750

An oak stool on solid notched ends, circa 1600, 20¼in. wide. £825

Victorian mahogany revolving piano stool, 1860. £85

One of a pair of George III mahogany stools, one branded VR BP N22224 1866, 23½in. wide. £12,960

One of a set of six 17th century oak joint stools, 18in. wide. £25,920

STOOLS

A walnut stool, the oval padded seat on splayed club legs and pad feet, 20in. wide. £1,190

A George III mahogany window seat with serpentine seat covered in gold damask, 37in. wide. £9,350

A Jacobean oak stool with carved and turned supports. £2,000

A George I walnut stool with drop-in seat covered with floral petit point needlework, 22in. wide. £11,880

One of a pair of George III pine window seats with differently upholstered bowed seats and double-scrolled ends, 48½in. wide. £5,940

A George I gilt gesso stool with drop-in seat, 24½in. wide. £22,680

An early 17th century oak joint stool on fluted tapering legs joined by plain stretchers, 17in. wide. £700

A Middle Eastern hardwood stool with saddle seat, inlaid with ivory stylised flowerheads, 17in. wide. £430

A 17th century oak joint stool with ring-turned legs joined by plain stretchers, 17¼in. wide. £1,025

SUITES

A suite of George III mahogany seat furniture comprising a set of four library armchairs, upholstered in gros and petit-point needlework, a window seat and a sofa, the window seat 51in. wide, the sofa 84in. wide.   £32,400

Part of a suite of early George III mahogany seat furniture, the sofa with serpentine back and seat, 84in. long.   £36,000

A mid 19th century suite of giltwood seat furniture, comprising: a settee and four open arm elbow chairs on fluted and turned legs.   £7,500

SUITES

Part of a 20th century seven-piece rattan porch set, settee 56in. wide.
£655

An Edwardian mahogany drawingroom suite of seven pieces, with satinwood panel and boxwood string inlay.   £1,000

Early 20th century group of carved bear furniture of Swiss origin.
£2,390

175

Early 20th century three-piece Louis XV-style giltwood parlour set, including settee, armchair and side chair, upholstered in gold silk brocade, settee 42in. long.   £1,660

Part of an Edwardian Art Nouveau mahogany inlaid seven-piece suite, comprising a two-seat settee, two tub chairs and four single chairs.   £600

A 19th century suite of Louis XV-style giltwood seat furniture, comprising a canape and four fauteuils, upholstered in 19th century Aubusson tapestry.   £1,700

Two of a set of six 18th century German walnut fauteuils and canape,
upholstered in gros and petit point needlework, the canape 51in. wide.
£4,970

Part of a suite of giltwood seat furniture of Louis XV design comprising: four fauteuils
and a canape, each upholstered in floral Aubusson tapestry.   £5,500

Part of a four-piece Harden & Co. livingroom set, comprising: settee, rocker and two
armchairs, settee 54in. wide, circa 1910.   £1,105

Two of a set of six early George III mahogany dining chairs, the seats covered in gros point floral needlework and a humpback sofa , 78in. wide.   £23,220

A beechwood salon suite painted to simulate mahogany, manufactured by Jacob & Josef Kohn, width of sofa 122cm.   £755

Two of a set of eight open armchairs, one of three window seats and a sofa all with caned seats with squab cushions, the sofa 72½in. wide.   £42,875

SUITES

A mahogany sofa and two side chairs of horseshoe shape, designed by
Josef Hoffmann, sofa 121cm. wide.   £3,780

Part of a seven-piece Renaissance Revival walnut and burl veneer parlour set, consisting of
sofa, 73in. long, two armchairs and four side chairs, America, circa 1860.   £1,485

Part of an Edwardian inlaid part-upholstered drawingroom suite comprising
settee, two armchairs and four singles with green velvet upholstery.   £875

ARCHITECT'S TABLES

A George II mahogany architect's table with adjustable hinged top, 2ft.8in. wide, circa 1760.   £6,160

George III mahogany architect's portable table.   £350

A mid Georgian walnut architect's table, the frieze drawer with leather lined slide and swivelling ink drawer, 33in. wide.   £4,105

Early 18th century architect's walnut veneered table, with hinged adjustable top, 31in. wide.   £6,000

A late George II mahogany architect's table with fitted interior and a candlestand, 3ft. wide, circa 1750.   £1,760

A George II walnut architect's table with brass candle slides, 3ft. wide.   £3,000

A George III mahogany architect's table with adjustable top above a pull-out front section fitted with compartments, 37½in. wide.   £2,860

A mid Georgian mahogany and rosewood crossbanded architect's table, 37in. wide.   £2,915

A George III mahogany architect's table with double easel top and a frieze drawer, 35½in. wide.   £3,025

CARD & TEA TABLES

An early Victorian mahogany tea table with swivel and flap top, 3ft. wide.
£300

A Federal mahogany sofa card table, the top with shaped leaves, circa 1810/30, 51½in. wide, open.
£760

A George III kingwood and satinwood card table, with baize lined crossbanded top, 36½in. wide.
£1,080

A Chippendale tilt-top mahogany tea table, Mass., 1760-80, 32in. diam.
£2,870

One of a pair of early 19th century mahogany card tables, 34¾in. wide.
£11,880

Mid 18th century George III walnut 'Isle of Man' tilt-top tea table, 31¾in. diam.
£3,015

A mid Georgian mahogany combined card and tea table with candle sconces, possibly Irish, 35in. wide.
£3,240

A George II red walnut demi-lune tea table with fold-over top, 74cm. wide, circa 1740.
£1,815

A George I walnut tea/games table with lobed triple-flap top, 33in. wide.
£5,185

CARD & TEA TABLES

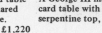
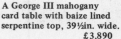

A Federal mahogany card table, attributed to Chas. H. Lannvier, circa 1800-15, 36in. wide. £2,140

A Regency rosewood card table with fold-over top on squared baluster column, 3ft. wide. £1,220

A George III mahogany card table with baize lined serpentine top, 39½in. wide. £3,890

A George III mahogany and crossbanded rectangular card table with lined folding top, 35¾in. wide. £500

A George III satinwood, crossbanded and painted D-shaped card table with fold-over top, 39in. wide. £3,000

A George II mahogany card table, the baize lined rectangular top with ribbon-and-rosette border, 35½in. wide. £10,800

A George II mahogany card table with baize lined interior, 31in. wide. £1,870

A Regency brass inlaid and rosewood tea table with twin-flap swivelling top, 35½in. wide. £2,160

A Federal mahogany card table, the lift top with D-shaped front and sides, Boston, circa 1795, 35in. wide. £2,885

CARD & TEA TABLES

One of a pair of George III mahogany tea tables on square tapering legs, 36in. wide. £5,400

A classical Revival mahogany and mahogany veneered card table with D-shaped top, N.Y., circa 1810, 36in. wide. £3,125

A Regency penwork card table with swivelling top, 36in. wide. £755

A George II mahogany chinoiserie 'concertina-action' card table, circa 1750, 2ft. 11½in. wide. £1,045

A George III satinwood and fruitwood card table with baize lined crossbanded D-shaped top, 36in. wide. £2,050

Late 18th century George II walnut games table, 34in. wide. £2,305

A laburnum and walnut card table, the baize lined top with candle roundels and guinea wells, 34in. wide. £7,700

A late Federal mahogany card table with hinged D-shaped top, Mass., 1820-30, 36in. wide. £1,365

A George II mahogany tea table with shaped eared top and concertina action, 33in. wide. £2,160

CARD & TEA TABLES

A Regency D-shaped card table banded and inlaid with satinwood lines, 35in. wide. £1,945

One of a pair of Regency rosewood card tables with hinged D-shaped baize lined tops, 35¾in. wide. £3,455

A George III satinwood card table with baize lined top and the drawer with chased silvered handles, 38½in. wide. £2,810

A Federal mahogany and mahogany veneer card table with lift top, circa 1795, 34½in. wide. £3,055

A Chippendale mahogany tilt-top tea table, probably Newport, Rhode Island, 1760-80, 30¾in. diam. £725

A Federal mahogany card table, the top with canted corners, N.Y., 1800-20, 35in. wide. £1,540

A Regency ormolu mounted calamander card table with baize lined D-shaped folding top, 38in. wide. £7,560

A George II mahogany tea table with shaped fold-over top, the drawer with brass drop handle, 28½in. wide. £1,100

A George III satinwood and calamander card table, the top with fan inlay, 35½in. wide. £3,890

CARD & TEA TABLES

A Regency rosewood card table, the baize lined top with boxwood stringing, 36in. wide. £2,050

A George III mahogany tea table with eared folding top and frieze drawer, 34in. wide. £1,870

A George III satinwood card table, circa 1785, 2ft.11½in. wide. £1,980

A walnut card table, the hinged top enclosing a panel of needlework in gros and petit point, 34½in. wide. £1,405

George III style mahogany galleried tea table on three carved ogee legs, England, 27½in. wide. £700

An early Georgian calamander wood and walnut card table, the top with candle sconces and guinea wells, 34in. wide. £7,020

A George II mahogany tea table with eared folding top, 32in. wide. £3,025

A Chippendale mahogany tilt-top tea table, Mass., 1770-85, top 30.1/3 x 30in. £20,015

A Sheraton period mahogany fold-over top demi-lune card table with rosewood crossbanding. £500

CENTRE TABLES

A Regency mahogany centre table with tip-up top on a ring-turned baluster shaft and quadrapartite base, 50in. diam. £1,780

A Victorian satinwood, ebony and marquetry centre table with waved frieze, 42in. wide. £2,810

A Regency and parcel gilt plum-pudding mahogany centre table, 50½in. diam. £5,400

A mid 18th century mahogany silver or centre table, circa 1740, possibly Cork, 2ft.7in. wide. £2,090

A rosewood centre table, the top inlaid with specimen marbles and semi-precious stones, 23in. wide. £3,455

A Louis XV fruitwood table with a small drawer at either end, 39in. long. £350

An early 19th century Tyrolean parquetry centre table on a scrolled tripartite base, 31½in. diam. £970

An oak centre table framed by chequered inlaid lines executed by Peter Waals assisted by P. Burchett, 1928, 68.3cm. wide. £1,510

A Victorian mahogany centre table with marble and semi-precious stone top, 27in. diam. £4,860

CENTRE TABLES

A mid Victorian ormolu mounted thuya and marquetry centre table attributed to Holland & Sons, 51½in. diam. **£8,100**

A gilt and green japanned centre table on cabriole legs, possibly German, 41in. wide. **£1,980**

A Regency brass inlaid rosewood centre table with tip-up top, 50½in. diam. **£2,700**

A black and gold lacquer centre table of early Georgian design, 34in. wide. **£1,510**

A rosewood centre table, the square top inset with specimen marble, 15½in. square. **£1,350**

A Queen Anne giltwood centre table, the top with geometric strapwork foliage and shells, 30in. wide. **£3,780**

A Regency parcel gilt, mahogany and ebony centre table, the circular black fossil marble top with pierced brass border, 25in. diam. **£9,720**

An ormolu mounted tulipwood and ebony centre table with inset breccia marble top, 28.5in. wide. **£3,300**

A Regency rosewood, satinwood, mahogany and amboyna centre table, 26in. diam. **£1,190**

CENTRE TABLES

A mid Victorian gilt metal mounted amboyna and marquetry centre table, 42¼in. wide. £2,200

A William IV walnut centre table with octagonal specimen marble top bordered with black limestone, stamped Eastmure, 45in. wide. £30,800

A German walnut centre table on shackled slave legs, 51in. wide. £3,080

A Regency ormolu mounted mahogany centre table with grey marble top, 32½in. diam. £3,890

An early Victorian walnut centre table in the manner of Baldock, 35½in. diam. £2,860

A Biedermeier mahogany centre table with circular marble tray top, 36in. diam. £2,160

A Renaissance Revival walnut centre table, with variegated red and white marble insert, circa 1860, 36in. wide. £355

An ormolu and mahogany centre table of Louis XVI style, on twinned simulated bamboo legs, 27in. diam. £1,190

A Napoleon III ormolu and purple quartz centre table, twice stamped Monbro, 32in. wide. £10,450

CENTRE TABLES

An ormolu centre table in the style of Weisweiler, with inset marble top, 38in. wide.   £5,280

Renaissance Revival inlaid walnut centre table, circa 1870, 42¼in. wide. £1,110

A late 18th century Dutch marquetry inlaid tray-top serpentined centre table, 32½ x 22½in.   £575

A George III satinwood centre table, the tip-up top crossbanded with rosewood, 41in. diam. £7,020

One of a pair of gilt gesso centre tables with later inset honey-coloured marble tops, 21in. wide.   £5,400

An early Victorian ebonised and parcel gilt centre table with Italian scagliola top, 36¼in. diam.   £6,600

A George II mahogany centre table with rounded rectangular tray top, 30¼in. wide.   £770

A Victorian pollard oak and painted centre table, the top on a naturalistic bullrush pedestal, 28¾in. diam.   £11,000

An early 18th century boulle gilt metal and ebony centre table, the top inlaid with a berainesque scene, 37in. wide.   £1,730

CONSOLE TABLES

A mid 18th century giltwood console table, sold with another en suite of a later date, 41½in. wide. £4,860

One of a pair of Regency rosewood and parcel gilt console tables with white marble tops, 54in. wide. £6,265

A George II pine console table with moulded white and grey marble top, 48½in. wide. £30,800

A Regency simulated rosewood and parcel gilt console in the manner of Thos. Hope, 89cm. wide. £6,500

One of a pair of grained pine console tables with marble tops on carved eagle supports, 42¼in. wide. £2,375

A classical brass inlaid mahogany marble top pier table, N.Y., circa 1810/30, 41½in. wide. £1,820

A George II giltwood console table with black-veined yellow marble top, 2ft.9½in. wide, circa 1740. £1,180

One of a pair of Louis XV giltwood console tables with shaped breccia marble tops, 23½in. wide. £2,810

One of a pair of George II giltwood pier tables, each with D-shaped white marble top, 35in. wide. £118,800

CONSOLE TABLES

A 19th century giltwood and gesso serpentine fronted console table. **£500**

An early George II giltwood pier table, in the manner of Wm. Kent, 3ft.3¼in. wide, circa 1730. **£8,250**

A Classical Revival brass inlaid mahogany console table, 36in. wide. **£810**

A Louis XVI mahogany console desserte with brass mounts and grey veined marble top, 34in. wide. **£1,430**

One of a pair of giltwood console tables with serpentine moulded white tops, 40in. wide. **£2,810**

George II mahogany demi-lune lift-top console table on cabriole legs, circa 1750, 29½ x 14¾ x 29in. high. **£1,035**

A Louis XV Provincial walnut console table with later breccia marble top, 34½in. wide. **£1,080**

Late 18th century Italian parcel gilt and black painted console table with inset jasper top, 29½in. wide. **£2,860**

An 18th century Italian carved giltwood console table with a serpentine sienna marble top, 1.46m. long. **£1,100**

DINING TABLES

A William IV rosewood dining table with circular tilt-top , 55in. diam. **£900**

A Victorian mahogany extending dining table with concave-sided plinth bases, 58 x 166in. including four leaves. **£9,720**

A Restoration mahogany breakfast table with circular top, 45¼in. diam. **£1,836**

A George II mahogany tripod table with rectangular needlework top, 2ft.8½in. wide, circa 1750. **£5,060**

A Killarney yewwood pedestal table inlaid with satinwood stringing, circa 1840, 5ft. wide. **£1,300**

A Georgian mahogany circular snap-top dining table, 5ft.2in. diam. **£5,400**

A Renaissance Revival walnut and burl veneer dining table, the base separates to accommodate nine leaves, circa 1860. **£1,290**

Chippendale mahogany serpentine top tip table, Mass., circa 1780, 32½in. diam. **£1,333**

A Regency satinwood and mahogany breakfast table inlaid with ebonised lines, 57¼in. wide. **£3,850**

DINING TABLES

A Regency rosewood breakfast table, the top with burrelm banding on ring-turned ebonised shaft, 59½in. wide. £2,160

A Victorian walnut marble top table, America, circa 1870, top 44 x 28in. £650

A George III satinwood crossbanded mahogany breakfast table, 4ft.8in. wide, circa 1790. £3,300

Regency rosewood loo table with scroll feet, 1830. £845

An early 19th century figured mahogany octagonal pedestal tip table with brass castors, 42in. £700

A Victorian circular snaptop burr walnut veneered breakfast table, with cabriole legs, 4ft.6in. diam. £800

A Regency mahogany patent dining table, the handles inscribed G. Oakley, Maker, 57 x 147in. £15,120

A Victorian coromandel ebonised and parcel gilt loo table, 48in. diam. £800

A George III mahogany breakfast table, the crossbanded top with satinwood banding, 54¾in. wide. £2,052

DINING TABLES

A mahogany extending
dining table, circa 1840,
16ft. long.   £6,600

A Gustav Stickley round
library table, no. 633,
circa 1904, 48in. diam.
                    £1,180

A 19th century circular
mahogany extending
table, 60in. diam.
                    £1,200

A William IV rosewood
veneered circular snap-top
breakfast table, 4ft. diam.
                    £880

A maple and pine hutch
table, New England, circa
1780, 48in. diam. £653

A marquetry topped
centre table. £6,200

A Flemish oak dining table
with draw leaf top on cup
and cover legs, partly late
16th century, 100in. long
open.   £810

Round oak pedestal base
dining table, signed with
metal tag, circa 1908, 54in.
diam.   £979

An early Victorian mahogany
dining table, extending to
93in., including two extra
leaves.   £1,375

DINING TABLES

A George III rosewood and satinwood breakfast table with oval crossbanded tip-up top, 57in. wide. £8,100

Gustav Stickley hexagonal top library table, circa 1904, no. 625, 48in. diam. £3,986

A Regency mahogany breakfast table with circular tip-up top, 50½in. diam. £2,420

An early Victorian mahogany veneered circular snap-top breakfast table, 4ft.7in. diam. £820

A George III satinwood and inlaid breakfast table, crossbanded in tulipwood, with oval snap top, 1.23m. £8,500

A 19th century exhibition centre table, the top within a chequered ivory and ebony surround, 45in. diam. £6,000

An early 19th century German circular rosewood dining table, circa 1830, 3ft.6in. diam. £3,300

Mid Victorian oak dining table carved in Elizabethan style, extending with six leaves to 17ft.8in. £1,200

A mid Victorian burr walnut breakfast table with quarter veneered inlaid marquetry tilt-top, 60in. diam. £2,200

FURNITURE

A George III satinwood and rosewood breakfast table with tip-up top, 49½in. wide.   £9,560

A large carved oak dining table.   £600

A late George III mahogany breakfast table, the rounded rectangular top with yew-wood crossbanding, 40 x 58½in.   £1,100

A Regency circular mahogany and brass inlaid breakfast or dining table.   £1,050

A 19th century Celonise ebony centre table with peacock octagonal tilt-top, 39in. wide.   £3,300

Regency rosewood centre pedestal table, circa 1830.   £916

A George III satinwood and mahogany breakfast table with tip-up top, 53in. wide.   £5,184

A figured walnut snap-top dining table, 156cm. wide.   £2,800

A Renaissance Revival marble top parlour table, by T. Brooks Cabinet & Upholstery Warehouse, circa 1865, the white oval top 37in. long.   £753

DINING TABLES

A George III mahogany octagonal tip-up breakfast table, 42½in. wide. **£920**

Victorian oak draw-leaf table, circa 1900. **£100**

A rosewood and brass inlaid breakfast table in the Regency taste, 1.24m. diam. **£3,000**

A 19th century circular mahogany tip-top dining table with lion's paw feet, 52in. diam. **£340**

Late 19th century amboyna-wood octagonal breakfast table with ebonised borders, 48in. wide. **£950**

A Regency circular breakfast table in rosewood with a beaded edge, 52in. diam. **£7,400**

A late Georgian circular mahogany breakfast table centred by an inlaid floral medallion, 55in. diam. **£820**

A mid Victorian walnut and inlaid loo table, 48in. wide. **£360**

A Regency rosewood brass inlaid centre table with circular tip-up top, 48½in. diam. **£5,720**

DRESSING TABLES

Victorian walnut and ebony dressing table, 1860. £420

Late Victorian walnut dressing table, 1880. £250

Victorian oak dressing table, 1880. £150

A George III satinwood dressing table edged with stringing, raised on six square tapering supports, 32¾in. wide. £1,980

A green and gold lacquer, serpentine top, dressing table with chinoiserie decoration and pull-out writing slide, 31½in. wide. £1,295

A George III mahogany dressing chest, the hinged top enclosing a fitted interior with an easel mirror, 24½in. wide. £3,205

A Chippendale carved walnut dressing table, Phila., 1765-85, 36in. wide. £155,215

Mid 19th century carved walnut marble top shaving stand, America, 58¼in. high. £835

Queen Anne tiger maple dressing table, circa 1760, 28½in. wide. £2,500

DRESSING TABLES

Early 19th century Empire crotched walnut dressing table, France, 28in. wide.
£500

A small Victorian Duchess dressing table, 1860. £970

Victorian mahogany dressing table, 1860.   £450

A George III mahogany, gentleman's enclosed dressing table, 30in. wide.
£485

Late 18th century George III mahogany dressing table, the hinged top opens to reveal a fitted interior, 24in. wide.
£665

A Sheraton period mahogany tulipwood crossbanded and chequerstrung serpentine front enclosed dressing table, 75cm. wide.   £2,000

A Country Queen Anne cherry dressing table, central Mass., circa 1800, 24in. wide.   £3,300

A George IV mahogany dressing table with oblong swing mirror, 48in. wide.
£600

A Louis XV amaranth, tulipwood and floral marquetry table de toilette by G. Peridiez, 35in. wide.   £4,535

DROP-LEAF TABLES

A Chippendale walnut drop-leaf dining table on Marlborough legs, 1765-85, 56in. long, extended. £2,215

A late George II mahogany two flap table with oval top, 49 x 59in. extended. £1,980

A Chippendale walnut dining table, circa 1770, 48½in. long. £4,165

A Queen Anne tiger maple and maple dining table, New England, circa 1760, 41½in. wide. £2,290

A classical carved mahogany drop-leaf table, circa 1815, 38in. wide. £650

A Queen Anne maple dining table with oval drop-leaf top, New England, circa 1760, 40½in. wide. £810

A Queen Anne maple tea table, New England, circa 1750, 29¼in. wide. £765

George II mahogany drop-leaf table raised on cabriole legs, circa 1750, 42in. wide. £1,405

A George II triangular mahogany table with curved flaps. £2,300

DROP-LEAF TABLES

A Victorian walnut small oval Sutherland table, 1ft. 8½in. £300

A George III mahogany gate-leg dining table with twin flap top, 56in. wide open. £2,590

Federal mahogany drop-leaf dining table, America, circa 1795, 46 x 96in. £1,585

A Chippendale mahogany card table with scalloped front skirt, Mass., circa 1770, 31½in. wide. open. £4,235

A late Federal mahogany drop-leaf table, the top clover shaped, N.Y., 1800/20, 37in. wide. £240

A Federal mahogany break-fast table with D-shaped leaves, 1800-15, 45in. wide, open. £2,155

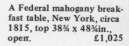

A Chippendale mahogany dining table with two drop-leaves, Phila., 1765-85, 55in. long. £915

A Queen Anne maple dining table with circular drop-leaf, circa 1760, 41¾in. wide. £5,405

A Federal mahogany break-fast table, New York, circa 1815, top 38¾ x 48¾in., open. £1,025

DRUM-TOP TABLES

A 19th century mahogany ebony strung and brass mounted drum top library table, 1.01m. diam. £2,400

A Sheraton design satinwood drum table on a turned, fluted and writhen column, 23in. diam. £850

An early Victorian mahogany drum table, the circular top lined in tooled brown leather, 53in. diam. £800

A George III mahogany drum table with revolving octagonal top, 43½in. wide. £8,640

A mahogany drum table with circular red leather lined top, 42in. diam. £2,750

A George III ormolu mounted rosewood library table with leather lined circular top, 44in. diam. £6,480

A George IV oak octagonal library table with leather lined top, 42½in. wide. £1,730

A Federal mahogany and veneer drum table on a tripod cabriole leg base, 31in. diam, circa 1820. £410

A George III mahogany drum table with leather lined revolving circular top, 38½in. diam. £4,860

GAMES TABLES

A mid Victorian black, gilt and mother-of-pearl japanned papier-mache pedestal table, 24½in. wide. **£880**

A George II mahogany games table, the hinged top enclosing a backgammon well, 36in. wide. **£1,945**

A mid Victorian black, gilt and mother-of-pearl japanned papier-mache games table, 19¾in. diam. **£770**

A late Regency rosewood, fruitwood and Tunbridgeware games table, 16¾in. square. **£2,700**

A Victorian walnut and parcel gilt etched pedestal games table with inset octagonal specimen marble top, 33in. wide. **£2,420**

A Victorian papier-mache games table, the revolving top inlaid for chess in mother-of-pearl, stamped Jennens & Bettridge, 67cm. wide. **£2,600**

Regency rosewood games table with tooled red leather top and fitted backgammon drawer. **£2,200**

An inlaid walnut games and work table of bow-ended form, 2ft.4in. wide, circa 1860. **£1,200**

An early Victorian rosewood work and games table with folding swivel top, 20in. wide. **£650**

GAMES TABLES

A Regency rosewood games/work table on a U-shape support, 26in. wide. £2,420

A 19th century walnut and fruitwood pictorial marquetry games table, 25in. diam. £1,430

A Country Federal painted tip table, the top with black and red painted chequerboard, top 19¼ x 19in. £1,110

A mahogany tric-trac table of Louis XVI style, the leather lined reversible tray top with ebony and fruitwood chess players, 44½in. wide. £1,980

A Regency penwork games table, on spirally-turned shaped ebonised shaft, 21½in. wide. £1,430

A George II mahogany triple folding top games table on cabriole legs, 34in. wide. £6,200

A Regency satinwood games and work table with lift-out top crossbanded with rosewood and inlaid on the reverse with a chessboard, 20in. wide. £3,080

A Jaipur marble games table, top inlaid with polychrome marbles, including lapis lazuli and coloured quartz, 25½in. sq. £2,200

A late Federal mahogany work table with two drop-leaves, N.Y., 1810-30, 38¾in. wide open. £1,730

GAMES TABLES

A Regency grained work
table, the penwork top
decorated as a games board,
16½in. wide.   £770

Victorian padoukwood
games table, 1850. £170

A Regency faded mahogany
and rosewood work table
on trestle ends and arched
tapering feet, 20in. wide.
                    £2,200

A Regency mahogany games
table inlaid with ebonised
lines and with reversible
centre section, 42½in. high.
                  £11,000

A Regency mahogany com-
bined games and work table,
the sides with candle-slides,
19in. wide.   £4,105

A 19th century Netherlands
rococo style mahogany in-
laid games table, top 34 x
31in.   £490

A George II mahogany, triple
fold-over, shaped top tea/
games table, 2ft.7½in. wide.
                    £5,200

A Chinese Export lacquer
games table, the top with
reversible lift-out centre
enclosing chess squares
and a backgammon board,
circa 1820, 35½in. wide.
                    £1,945

An Anglo-Indian ebony,
ivory and penwork games
table with rounded rect-
angular top inlaid with a
chessboard, 21in. square.
                    £1,820

GATELEG TABLES

A William and Mary padoukwood and oak gateleg dining table with oval twin-flap top, 56in. wide, open. £3,455

An oak gateleg dining table with oval twin-flap top and bobbin-turned frame, 17th century, 70in. wide, open. £2,810

A Charles II oak gateleg table with oval twin-flap top, some later supports and later bun feet, 71½in. wide, open. £3,960

An oak gateleg dining table with oval twin-flap top, part 17th century, 80in. long. £1,000

A George III mahogany gateleg dining table with oval twin-flap top and two fielded frieze drawers, 53in. diam., open. £15,120

A late 17th century oak oval twin-flap top gateleg table, the friezes with a drawer each end, 4ft.6in. x 5ft. £2,600

A William and Mary walnut gateleg table with moulded twin-flap sixteen-sided top and bobbin-turned frame, 42½in. wide. £7,560

A William and Mary oak gateleg table with oval top, fitted with two drawers, 41 x 40in. £495

GATELEG TABLES

A large oak gateleg dining table with twin-flap rectangular top, 66in. wide, open. £1,945

An oak gateleg dining table with oval twin-flap top, 17th century, 75in. wide. £2,160

A 17th century yewwood gateleg dining table, 57in. wide, open. £3,025

An oak two-flap gateleg table on barley sugar twist supports, 4ft. x 4ft.9in. £580

An oak gateleg table with oval twin-flap top, 17th century, 56½in. long. £1,100

A mid Georgian red walnut gateleg table with oval twin-flap top on scroll headed cabriole legs, 57in. wide, open. £3,080

Late 17th century oak gateleg table with oval twin-flap top and frieze drawer, possibly Dutch, 49½in. wide. £1,870

A mid Georgian mahogany gateleg table with oval twin-flap top, on club legs and pad feet, 56in. wide, open. £2,200

A mid Victorian burr walnut dining table on fluted and turned twin-column supports and scrolled feet, 96in. long. £2,090

A George III mahogany serving table, the serpentine top with chamfered corners, 70in. wide. £2,810

A late George III mahogany twin-pedestal dining table, 105½ x 48in., including three extra leaves. £5,500

A George III mahogany dining table with wide darker mahogany borders, fully extended 122in. £1,750

A Regency mahogany patent dining table with D-shaped end-sections, 45¾ x 113½in. £2,810

A George III style mahogany three-pillar dining table with D-ended top, 140in. x 46in. £2,640

An early Victorian figured mahogany extending dining table, the oval ends with five extra leaves, stamped Cope & Collinson, 12ft.4in. long, extended. £3,100

A George III mahogany D-end dining table in three sections, the centre with two flaps above a plain frieze on square tapering legs, 106in. £2,200

FURNITURE

LARGE TABLES

Late 19th century 'Monarch' marquetry and cast iron pool table, by Brunswick & Balke-Collender Co., Buffalo, 9ft. x 4½ft. £10,950

A George III mahogany dining table with five pillar supports, 183in., fully extended, the two extra leaves and pillars unillustrated.
£38,500

A Regency mahogany patent Imperial dining table in the manner of Gillows, 66in. wide, 174½in. extended.   £10,260

An early 17th century oak refectory table, 18ft.2in. x 3ft.5in.   £6,000

A mahogany dining table with D-shaped end-sections, 54 x 98in., including two extra leaves.   £2,700

A Regency mahogany three-pedestal dining table with rounded rectangular end-sections on baluster shafts and splayed bases, 53½ x 196in.   £7,560

George II Cuban mahogany swing leg dining table, the oval top opening to 5ft. £2,600

A William IV oak extending dining table, with three leaves, 53¼in. wide, 99½in. long.
£3,080

LARGE TABLES

An oval dining table, the frieze inlaid with stringing, on brass castors, 43½ x 55in.
£1,320

William and Mary walnut tavern table, the top with breadboard ends, Pennsylvania, circa 1740, 71½in. long.
£2,600

A George III mahogany D-end dining table, 9ft.6in. including leaf insertion, circa 1790.
£11,550

A 17th century and later oak refectory table with rectangular top, 119in. long.
£1,945

An early 19th century D-ended mahogany dining table.
£2,000

A George III mahogany serpentine serving table with fluted frieze, 103in. long.
£9,350

One of a pair of George III giltwood side tables designed by Robt. Adam and made by S. Alken, 65½in. long.
£286,000

A Regency mahogany drop-leaf table on turned tapering ribbed legs, 70½in. long.
£3,520

LARGE TABLES

A George III yewwood serpentine serving table with eared top and fluted frieze flanked and divided by roundels, 83½in. long. £8,250

An oak draw-leaf table on baluster turned legs joined by box stretcher, basically 17th century, 72in. wide, extended. £1,100

Large Queen Anne style mahogany oval drop-leaf table, 83¼in. long. £1,820

Early 20th century mahogany library table with leather inset top, by Waring & Gillows, 8ft. x 4ft. £800

An Empire carved mahogany three-part dining table, 1825-35, 111½in. long, top extended. £3,210

A Regency mahogany patent dining table with D-shaped ends, 53 x 123in. £14,040

A Regency rosewood veneered platform base extending dining table, the splayed legs with brass sabots on castors, 4ft.2in. x 8ft.4in. extended. £2,300

A Regency mahogany twin pedestal dining table, on ring turned column and quadruped hipped splayed legs, 2.41 x 1.33m. overall. £3,600

LARGE TABLES

A George III mahogany three-pillar dining table with D-shaped ends, 53½ x 145in. **£10,000**

A George III mahogany serpentine serving table with brass rail at the back, 97in. long. **£8,800**

A George IV mahogany extending dining table, the top with two drop leaves on seven turned and ribbed tapering legs, 132in. long extended. **£3,300**

A mahogany dining table of early Georgian style in two sections, each drop-leaf section with twin-flap rectangular top, 96in. long. **£8,500**

A Regency padoukwood and mahogany patent dining table, 154in. long, including four leaves. **£14,040**

A Regency mahogany dining table with ring-turned baluster shafts and quadripartite bases, 52½ x 125in. **£8,100**

A George III mahogany bow-ended sectional dining table, 4ft.5in. x 7ft.2in. **£2,800**

A Regency mahogany and ebony strung D-end dining table in three sections, centre section with reconstruction, 1.87 x 1.22m. extended. **£3,600**

LARGE TABLES

One of a pair of George III mahogany serpentine serving tables, 67in. wide. £12,100

A Regency ormolu mounted mahogany breakfront serving table, 81in. wide. £9,350

A George III oval snap-top dining table with a reeded edge, 4ft.1in. x 5ft.8in. £3,400

A Georgian D-ended mahogany dining table, the friezes with rosewood bands, 8ft.8in. long. £1,000

A George III Irish mahogany drop-leaf dining table of 'Hunt' or 'Wake' type, 2.75 x 1.36m. £16,000

A mahogany three-pillar dining table, the rounded rectangular top with a reeded edge, 150in. long, including two leaves. £1,600

A late 17th/early 18th century solid walnut centre refectory table with two-plank top, 30¼ x 77½in. £2,860

A mid 19th century Shaker Community table, possibly New Hampshire, 21ft.3in. long. £26,760

OCCASIONAL TABLES

George II mahogany pie-
crust tilt-top table, circa
1760, 25½in. diam.
£1,665

A Chippendale mahogany
tilt-top tea table, Mass.,
1760-80, 29in. wide.
£1,070

A mahogany tripod table,
the legs carved with lion
mask shoulders on paw feet,
32½in. wide.   £1,295

A William and Mary maple
tavern table, New England,
circa 1730, 34in. diam.
£3,885

A Federal mahogany tilt-
top table, circa 1800-20,
top 34 x 22½in.   £725

A Federal carved mahogany
serving table with D-shaped
top, 1810-15, 36in. wide.
£1,835

A mahogany and beechwood
small table with circular tray
top and baluster shaft with
leather foot rest on four legs
carved as boots, 15in. diam.
£430

An Art Deco coffee table,
circular parquetry top on
four scrolling wrought iron
legs, 79.6cm. diam.   £430

A Regency rosewood tripod
table with marble top,
20½in. wide.   £3,456

OCCASIONAL TABLES

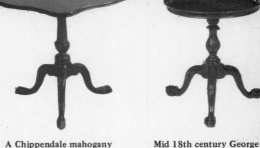

A George II mahogany tripod table with a baluster gallery, 2ft.1in. wide, circa 1755.   £2,200

A Chippendale mahogany tilt-top tea table, circa 1770-85, top 34 x 33½in.   £2,140

Mid 18th century George II mahogany tripod table, 2ft.2½in. diam.   £13,200

An early 19th century Chinese Export bamboo low table with later square top, 15¾in. square.   £540

A George III mahogany tripod table on a baluster stem and tripod base, 26 x 22in.   £420

An Emile Galle oak and marquetry table a deux plateaux, 60.2cm. wide.   £530

A George III mahogany tripod table with webbed claw and ball feet, 16½in. diam.   £1,300

A brushed steel and chromium-plated table, the design attributed to Ringo Starr, 121.5cm. wide, 66cm. high.   £220

One of a pair of Regency rosewood and parcel gilt lamp tables, 15½in. wide.   £4,320

OCCASIONAL TABLES

An Emile Galle fruitwood and marquetry table a deux plateaux, 52.5cm. wide.
£560

A 19th century carved Chippendale mahogany tea table with hinged top, 30in. diam.
£395

A mahogany urn table, the top with pierced fretwork gallery, 13in. square.
£1,620

A George III mahogany tripod table with scalloped circular tip-up top, 25½in. diam.
£3,080

A Queen Anne maple tea table, the skirt with crenelated edge, 28½in. wide.
£760

A Chippendale mahogany tilt-top tea table, Penn., 1760-80, 29in. high.
£1,525

A late 18th/early 19th century Chinese coromandel and lacquer occasional table, 47cm. sq.
£850

A padoukwood and mother-of-pearl inlaid tripod table with tip-up top, 38in. diam.
£480

A George III yewwood occasional table, the top inlaid with squares of specimen woods, 20½in. wide. £3,240

OCCASIONAL TABLES

A Galle mahogany and mar-
quetry two-tier etagere,
signed in the marquetry
Galle, 59.3cm. wide. £1,835

A revolving mahogany tip-up,
tray top table on turned tripod base, 32in. diam. £1,200

A mahogany occasional table
with circular galleried top
and fluted frieze, 23¼in.
diam.   £330

A Chippendale mahogany
birdcage tea table with
circular tilt-top, 1760-80,
33in. diam.   £2,445

A table with glazed, brass
framed, hide top supported
on elephant feet, 27in. wide.
                    £485

A Chippendale carved mahogany tea table with circular
top, Mass., 1765-85, 29½in.
diam.   £1,450

A Regency mahogany table
with rectangular top and
ring-turned tapering legs,
24in. wide.   £430

A mahogany circular snap-
top galleried occasional table,
32in. diam.   £1,300

A circular vitrine in mahogany with ormolu mounts,
24in. diam.   £460

OCCASIONAL TABLES

An ormolu gueridon in the manner of Weisweiler with pink granite top, stamped P. Sormani, Paris, 19¾in. diam.   £13,200

Queen Anne figured maple tea table, Massa., circa 1740, top 27½ x 17½in.
          £4,860

A Regency ormolu mounted mahogany and bronze gueridon in the manner of Thos. Hope, 21¼in. diam., 32¼in. high.
          £35,200

A set of four satinwood quartetto tables, the tops with ebony stringing, 14in. to 19½in.   £3,455

A 17th century oak chair table , the whole raised on turned legs with sleigh feet.   £1,500

Queen Anne tiger maple and maple tea table, New England, circa 1760, 31½ x 21½in.
          £2,460

A George II mahogany tripod table, the top with pierced fretwork gallery, 15in. diam., 24½in. high.
          £1,620

A Chippendale period mahogany snap-top table, 34½in. diam.   £800

Late 18th century Italian fruitwood tripod table with four frieze drawers.
          £1,295

OCCASIONAL TABLES

A George III satinwood tripod table, the tip-up top crossbanded with tulipwood, 21½in. wide.   £9,900

A George II red walnut occasional table supported on four cabriole legs, 47 x 21in.   £4,000

Victorian octagonal table inlaid with various woods, 1860.   £250

A Victorian walnut occasional table, labelled Plucknett & Steevens, Cabinet Makers & Upholsterers, Warwick & Leamington, 28in. high. £770

A Georgian style walnut wine table with two tiers of revolving book racks, 30in. high.   £490

A set of four mahogany quartetto tables with twin-turned spreading trestle ends, 11½in. to 18in.   £1,540

An early Victorian black and gilt japanned papier-mache pedestal table, 24in. wide.   £4,950

A George III mahogany birdcage table, the tilt-top with a gadrooned border, 2ft.3in. diam.   £420

A Federal cherry inlaid tip table, circa 1790, 28½in. high.   £1,595

OCCASIONAL TABLES

Gustav Stickley cut-corner library table, 1902-04, 48in. wide.   £525

An early Victorian ebony and marquetry octagonal library table by Edward Holmes Baldock, banded with kingwood, 58in. wide.   £7,700

A bamboo pattern centre table, the glazed top inset with a panel of 18th century Chinese painting on silk, 37¾in. wide.   £3,240

A Regency penwork and ebonised table, the octangular top with a temple in a landscape, 18½in. wide.   £1,980

A George III kidney shape occasional table in kingwood and rosewood, 37½in. wide.   £4,950

A 19th century carved rosewood, brass embellished and inlaid marble top occasional table.   £2,200

Country Chippendale maple table, New England, circa 1780, 26in. wide.   £1,265

A late Victorian mahogany specimen marble occasional table, 21in. wide.   £1,980

A black lacquer and simulated bamboo two-tier occasional table, 23¼in. wide.   £1,100

OCCASIONAL TABLES

A walnut draw-leaf table, Switzerland, circa 1700, top 43 x 30in.   £2,990

A mid 18th century rococo walnut table with twin-scalloped top, 60in. wide.   £12,960

An early 17th century Spanish painted walnut trestle table, 3ft.7in. long.   £1,100

One of a pair of parcel gilt and rosewood tripod tables with leather lined tops, 16¼in. diam.   £2,090

A George I red walnut silver table on cabriole legs, 2ft. 7½in. wide, circa 1725.   £1,100

Early 19th century rosewood tripod table, the top centred by a glazed panel enclosing a Viennese porcelain plate, 13in. sq.   £5,500

A Queen Anne giltwood table on foliate cabriole legs and pad feet, 22in. wide.   £2,700

Early 19th century Anglo-Indian ebony and specimen wood table with hexagonal top, 23in. diam.   £1,510

A mahogany, ebonised and marquetry jardiniere in the style of Charles Bevan, 77.6cm. high.   £2,700

PEMBROKE TABLES

A mid 18th century Cuban mahogany Pembroke table on turned tapering supports, 30in. wide. £350

A George III mahogany Pembroke table, the twin-flap top with one bowed frieze drawer, 42½in. wide. £3,455

A late 18th century George III satinwood Pembroke table on square tapering legs. £1,320

A George III satinwood and fruitwood Pembroke table, on square tapering legs, 37½in. wide. £4,970

An early Victorian mahogany Pembroke work table with fall leaves, 1ft.7in. wide. £320

A George III satinwood and fruitwood Pembroke table on square tapering legs, 40in. wide. £10,800

A Regency rosewood and brass inlaid occasional table of serpentine outline, 26¾ x 37½in. extended. £7,700

A Federal inlaid mahogany Pembroke table, the oval top with two drop leaves, 1790-1810, 39¼in. wide, open. £5,800

A late George III mahogany Pembroke table, the flap top with fluted edge, 35¾ x 39in. extended. £550

PEMBROKE TABLES

An early George III mahogany Pembroke table with serpentine twin-flap top, 34in. wide, open.   £1,135

A Federal inlaid mahogany Pembroke table, Mass., 1790/1810, 31in. wide.   £1,365

A Regency mahogany Pembroke table with rosewood banded twin-flap top, 37¼in. wide.   £330

A George III mahogany Pembroke table, the oval twin-flap top crossbanded in satinwood, 36½in. wide, open.   £1,510

A George III mahogany Pembroke table, the oval top with narrow kingwood crossbanding, 36½in. long extended.   £3,960

A painted satinwood Pembroke table, the oval twin-flap top crossbanded with rosewood. 36in. wide, open.   £4,620

A late Federal mahogany Pembroke table with clover shaped top, 1815-25, 40¾in. long, top extended.   £840

A 19th century satinwood and decorated Pembroke table, 99 x 80cm. extended.   £4,000

A Federal mahogany Pembroke table with two drop leaves, 1790-1810, 35in. wide. £1,985

SIDE TABLES

A laburnum and walnut side table with associated oyster-veneered top, basically late 17th century, 35¾in. wide. £3,080

An early 18th century walnut side table inlaid with feather banding, 38¼in. wide. £550

A scarlet and gold lacquer side table, basically late 17th century, 32½in. wide. £1,405

A Dutch walnut and marquetry side table on cabriole legs and pointed pad feet, 34in. wide. £2,050

A Regency ebony and mahogany side table, the turned tapering legs with ribbed collars, 20in. wide. £3,890

A William and Mary oak side table banded with walnut and inlaid with boxwood lines, 25¾in. wide. £1,295

An early Georgian walnut side table on cabriole legs and pad feet, 27½in. wide. £1,405

A Regency black painted and gilded side table in the Brighton Pavilion taste, 38in. wide. £4,180

One of a pair of parcel gilt and bronzed side tables with mottled green marble tops, 34½in. wide. £7,020

SIDE TABLES

An early Georgian walnut
side table, the top with
later carved border, 30in.
wide.   £1,025

An early George III maho-
gany side table with bowed
serpentine top, 30½in. wide.
£2,590

A Dutch walnut and floral
marquetry side table,
33¾in. wide.   £1,980

A 17th century oak side
table, the D-shaped top with
a flap at the back, 37¼in.
wide.   £4,320

One of a pair of gilt gesso
side tables with breccia
marble tops, on cabriole
legs and pad feet, 17½in.
wide.   £7,020

A Regency amboyna and
yewwood side table with
two frieze drawers,
35½in. wide.   £1,510

An early Georgian walnut
side table with carved border,
formerly a card table, 33in.
wide.   £1,025

Victorian carved oak side
table, 1860.   £460

One of a pair of Queen Anne
gilt gesso side tables, 27½in.
wide.   £38,880

SOFA TABLES

A Regency yewwood sofa table with twin-flap top, on reeded splayed legs, 64½in. wide, open. £2,810

A George IV painted elm and marquetry sofa table with twin-flap top, 57in. wide, open. £3,780

A Regency rosewood and satinwood sofa table with trestle ends and splayed feet, 58in. wide, open. £5,400

A Regency rosewood sofa table with brass stringing, on reel turned baluster column and quartette supports, 5ft. x 2ft.3in. £600

A Regency satinwood sofa table with rosewood cross-banding to the two-flap top, 37 x 26¼in. deep and 57½in. extended. £1,760

A Regency rosewood sofa table crossbanded in satin-wood and with box and ebony outlining, 153cm. wide, ex-tended. £7,200

A Scottish George III maho-gany sofa table, stamped Bruce EdinH, 63in. wide, open. £5,400

A Regency rosewood sofa table, inlaid with brass in stylised foliate design, 36½ x 59in. extended.£1,870

A George III rosewood sofa table with twin-flap top and two cedar lined frieze drawers, 54in. wide. £3,890

226

SOFA TABLES

A Regency black and gold lacquer sofa table with brass bordered twin-flap top, 61½in. wide, open. £6,480

A Regency maplewood sofa table with twin-flap top, the tapering feet with claw castors, 63in. wide. £9,180

A Regency calamander sofa table, the twin-flap top crossbanded in satinwood, 59in. long. £4,860

A Regency mahogany sofa table with twin-flap top and one frieze drawer, 53in. wide, open. £2,810

A classical mahogany sofa table, the working drawer with a brass lion head pull, circa 1810/20, Phila., 42in. wide. £2,655

A Regency rosewood sofa table with twin-flap top and frieze drawers, 58in. wide, open. £10,800

A George IV mahogany sofa table with twin-flap top and two frieze drawers, the trade label R. Snowdon, Cabinet Maker and Appraiser, Northallerton., 62in. wide, open. £2,050

A Regency calamander sofa table with twin-flap top, 58in. wide. £10,800

A Regency rosewood sofa table, the solid trestle ends with scrolling bases, 58in. wide, open. £5,940

WORKBOXES

A late Federal mahogany
work table, New York, 1815-
25, 23in. wide.   £2,175

Early 20th century Regency
brass and ebony inlaid work
table, England, 23½in. wide.
£910

A Federal walnut and maple
work table, New England,
1815-25, 20in. wide.
£690

An Edwardian painted maple
work table, the top with
hinged flap, on square tapering legs, 21in. wide. £1,295

A Chippendale mahogany
and cherrywood sewing
table, New England, 1815-
25, 70½in. wide.   £460

A Federal curly and bird's-
eye maple and mahogany
work table, 1795, top 20½
x 17in.   £360

A classical Revival mahogany
work table, possibly Balti-
more, circa 1810, 27.3/8in.
wide.   £1,710

A classical gilt stencilled
rosewood sewing table,
probably N.Y., circa 1815/
30, 24¾in. wide.   £3,035

A Country Federal tiger maple
work table, New England, circa
1820, on simulated bamboo
legs, 17½in. wide.   £1,970

WORKBOXES

Federal cherry inlaid work
table, New Jersey, circa
1815, 27in. high. £1,120

Mid 19th century Regency
inlaid mahogany and maho-
gany veneer work table,
36in. wide.   £405

A Federal carved mahogany
work table, probably New
York, circa 1810, 22in.
wide.   £10,275

A Victorian rectangular inlaid
burr walnut needlework
table with hinged top, 24in.
wide.   £530

A mid Victorian black, gilt and
mother-of-pearl, japanned
papier mache pedestal sewing
box, 15in. wide.   £1,510

A George III satinwood and
fruitwood work table, the
top crossbanded with maple-
wood and tulipwood, 22in.
wide.   £4,320

A George IV rosewood sewing
table with velvet-lined
swivelling hinged top, with
pleated olive simulated-silk
basket, 21in. wide.   £660

A Victorian tole workbox,
the glazed octangular lid
decorated with a winter
scene, 19½in. wide. £920

A Regency beechwood and
oak work table with crossbanded, twin-flap rounded
top, 25½in. wide.   £550

WRITING TABLES

A Robert Thompson 'Mouseman' oak writing desk, signed with a carved mouse, 182.5cm. wide. £385

A George IV ebony inlaid mahogany library table, on trestle ends and bar feet, 57½in. long. £9,720

A Regency ormolu mounted rosewood writing table in the manner of John McLean, 42¼in. wide. £39,600

Victorian walnut writing table, 1870. £245.

A 19th century scarlet tortoiseshell and brass marquetry bureau mazarin in the manner of Boulle, 1.22m. wide. £4,000

A late Regency mahogany writing table, the top with fluted edge and inset tooled leather panel, 41in. wide. £990

An early Victorian bird's-eye maple writing table, 36½in. wide. £1,730

A George III mahogany writing table with revolving easel top, 25in. wide. £2,810

A Regency pollard oak and parcel gilt writing table, the top centred by a hinged easel, 31in. wide. £1,980

WRITING TABLES

A Renaissance Revival burled walnut library table, labelled by Alex. Roux, N.Y., circa 1860, 48in. wide. £1,450

An ormolu mounted mahogany bureau plat of Louis XVI style with five panelled drawers, 42in. wide. £2,160

A Regency ormolu mounted mahogany writing table, the top with pierced quatrefoil three-quarter gallery, 45in. wide. £8,100

A George III mahogany veneered rectangular writing table with inset gilt tooled green leather top, 3ft.3in. long. £1,000

An Edwardian satinwood, rosewood and marquetry Carlton House desk with leather lined easel, 49in. wide. £6,480

A mid Victorian ormolu mounted walnut and tulipwood writing table with leather lined top, 43in. wide. £6,050

A Louis XV kingwood and parquetry writing table on cabriole legs, 26in. wide. £5,940

A Sheraton period rosewood and inlaid combined work and writing table, 14.3/8in. x 18.1/8in. £1,800

A William and Mary walnut writing or card table, the top lined with crimson velvet, 30in. wide. £7,560

WRITING TABLES

A Regency mahogany Carlton House desk, in the manner of Gillows, 55½in. wide. £17,280

A Louis XIV marquetry bureau mazarin, the top with brass edge, 1.17m. wide. £12,500

A Regency maple and rosewood marquetry library table, on standard end supports, 1.30m. £5,600

Mid 18th century George III mahogany writing table, 44in. wide. £4,310

A mahogany Carlton House writing table in late George III-style decorated with ebony stringing, 56in. wide. £2,400

A satinwood writing table with leather lined top and two cedar-lined frieze drawers, 39in. wide. £9,180

One of a pair of George III serpentine tables in the manner of John Cobb, 2ft. 6in. wide, circa 1770. £20,000

A George III mahogany writing table with leather lined, kidney-shaped top, 40in. wide. £2,200

A mid Victorian ormolu mounted rosewood and satinwood writing table, on cabriole legs, 32½in. wide. £1,540

TEAPOYS

A Victorian burr walnut
teapoy with rising lid,
48cm. diam.   £520

An early Victorian rose-
wood teapoy on bun
feet.   £320

An early Victorian maho-
gany teapoy with circular
hinged lid, 17½in.   £390

A William IV walnut pedestal
teapoy, the interior fitted
with two cannisters and two
glass mixing bowls, stamped
Gillow, 28½in. high.   £700

An early Victorian walnut
pedestal teapoy, the hinged
panel lid enclosing a fitted
interior, 19½in. diam. £280

A Regency brass inlaid rosewood teapoy with Bramah
lock and carrying handles,
17½in. wide.   £2,375

Regency rosewood teapoy.
                    £1,520

A Regency mahogany teapoy,
the hinged top enclosing a
divided interior with later tin
liners, 20in. wide.   £2,375

Victorian rosewood
teapoy on scroll
feet, 1840.   £300

TRUNKS & COFFERS

A grain painted pine blanket chest with turned brass pulls on cut-out base, 36in. wide, circa 1810. £1,040

A George I oyster veneered walnut and king-wood coffer with a drawer, the sides with brass carrying handles, 47in. wide. £7,560

A Charles I oak chest with four-panel rectangular top, circa 1640, 4ft.4in. wide. £1,375

An oak and elmwood chest with simple panelled top and sides, 4ft.1in. wide, circa 1620. £770

A Chippendale painted pine blanket chest, attributed to the Himmelberger Shop, circa 1790, 51in. wide. £7,255

A 17th century inlaid walnut cassone, Italy, on hairy paw feet, 50¼in. wide. £360

An early Victorian oak coffer, the panels 16th century, 65in. wide. £3,980

A 17th century Spanish leather and brass decorated coffer, 47in. wide. £385

TRUNKS & COFFERS

A George II rosewood and maple blanket chest on moulded square legs, 49in. wide. £1,945

Late 16th century Momoyama period small coffer with hinged domed cover, 28.5 x 17 x 13cm. £550

A Chinese Export black and gold lacquer coffer decorated with foliage and with hinged lid, 36in. wide. £865

A Momoyama period black lacquer domed chest in hiramakie and takamakie and inlaid in shell, circa 1600, 52cm. wide. £2,200

A Kuwaiti Dowry chest richly decorated with ornate brass overlay. £1,350

An Italian walnut cassone, partly 17th century, 80in. wide. £4,400

A 17th century Spanish oak and walnut coffer with rectangular top, on block feet, 61in. wide. £700

An iron-bound round topped coffer chest, inscribed 'Clara Angela from Men Anno 1744 21 January'. £400

TRUNKS & COFFERS

`A 16th century heavy oak planked coffer, the corners with shaped iron bracket mounts, 56 x 28 x 23in. £700

A 17th century and later walnut cassone with panelled front, 67in. wide. £2,810

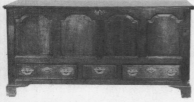

An 18th century oak dower chest with brass swan neck handles and pierced back plates, 5ft.4in. wide. £340

An 18th century oak dower chest with swan neck loop handles, 5ft.1in. wide. £320

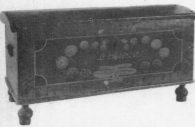

A Scandinavian painted dower chest with slightly domed, hinged top, dated 1828, 51in. wide. £565

A 17th century Spanish walnut coffer with plank top, 66½in. wide. £595

Late 18th century painted pine blanket chest on straight bracket feet, Penn., 33¼in. wide. £2,540

Early 18th century oak chest with panelled top enclosing an interior fitted with a well and two small drawers, 55½in. wide. £1,100

TRUNKS & COFFERS

Pine and white cedar board chest, the lift top with snipe hinges, probably Mass., circa 1700, 51in. wide.   £1,888

A late 17th century Swiss painted pine coffer with panelled rectangular top, 64in. wide.   £755

A partly 17th century walnut coffer on bun feet, 73in. wide.   £920

A putty painted pine blanket box, New England, late 18th century, 47in. wide.   £1,060

A 16th century Continental oak coffer, the top formed of three planks and with strap hinges, 5ft.10in. wide.   £2,100

An Italian walnut cassone with hinged top, 17th century and later, 67½in. wide.   £1,760

Mid 18th century black and gold lacquer coffer, mounted with shaped and engraved gilt brass angles and lock-plate, 56in. wide.   £11,000

An 18th century Dutch Colonial padoukwood blanket chest with pierced brass clasps and carrying handles, on bun feet, 67in. wide.   £1,085

WARDROBES

A Georgian mahogany sectional fitted wardrobe with four pairs of double doors, 80in. wide. £620

A Chippendale carved mahogany wardrobe, in two sections, New York, 1760-80, 53in. wide. £2,900

A mid Victorian mahogany cylinder wardrobe, the drawers with turned handles, 255cm. wide. £650

An 18th century Dutch figured walnut wardrobe, 6ft.3in. wide. £2,700

A bachelor's mahogany wardrobe, the doors opening to reveal four sliding trays, 52in. wide. £920

A George III gentleman's mahogany wardrobe with gilt brass cast swag handles, 4ft.2in. wide. £840

An early George III breakfront gentleman's wardrobe, 5ft.11in. wide, circa 1770. £2,750

Victorian carved walnut armoire, 1860. £190

A William and Mary gumwood kas in two sections, New York. 1725-55, 54in. wide. £2,755

WARDROBES

A Georgian mahogany
gent's wardrobe, the interior
fitted with brass hanging
rail, 51in. wide.   £425

An 18th century South
German figured and burr
walnut armoire, 74in. wide.
£14,300

An 18th century Scandin-
avian walnut armoire,
57in. wide.   £3,780

A George III mahogany and
satinwood crossbanded
gentleman's wardrobe, 4ft.
wide, circa 1780.   £1,080

Gustav Stickley two-door
wardrobe, panelled doors
opening to pull-out shelves,
1904, 33in. wide.   £1,050

An Empire Gothic maho-
gany wardrobe, signed by
Joseph Stewart Jr., New
York, and dated 1831,
69in. wide.   £2,810

A Regency period mahogany
breakfront wardrobe/linen
press, 8ft.2in. long. £2,000

A Louis XVI oak wardrobe
with moulded foliate cor-
nice. 61½in. wide. £1,945

A Regency mahogany break-
front wardrobe, 102in. wide.
£4,400

An early 19th century Dutch press with brass ring handles and lock plates, 6ft.1in. x 9ft. 8in. high.   £3,700

An 18th century Hepplewhite mahogany breakfront gentleman's wardrobe, 108in. wide. £2,000

An Edwardian mahogany wardrobe.   £880

An Aesthetic movement ash combination wardrobe and a similar dressing table, 43in. wide.   £320

A George III satinwood breakfront wardrobe inlaid with narrow bands and stringing, 104in. wide. £3,300

A Victorian walnut wardrobe with single large mirror panel door, 39in. wide.   £200

A 19th century gentleman's mahogany tray wardrobe, 4ft.1in. wide.   £1,000

An inlaid mahogany breakfront wardrobe, 88in. wide.   £2,200

A 'Mouseman' oak wardrobe by Robert Thompson, 1930's.   £600

WARDROBES

William and Mary poplar kas on bun feet, circa 1730, 72in. wide. £1,862

An Edwardian mahogany wardrobe by Edwards & Roberts, 50in. wide. £1,550

A Liberty & Co. inlaid mahogany armoire, England, circa 1905, 7ft. high. £385

A Gordon Russell oak wardrobe, together with an oak bed-head and end, 1930's, 138cm. wide. £500

Mid 20th century Sellers pollard elm and burr-walnut wardrobe with three panel doors, 82in. wide. £420

A 20th century mahogany hanging wardrobe with single shelf, 48in. wide. £550

An 18th century walnut veneered 'Frankfurter Nasenschrank', 222cm. high. £7,046

A Scandinavian painted kas, dated 1818, 67in. long. £1,820

A gentleman's rosewood, kingwood, parquetry inlaid and ormolu mounted wardrobe, 8ft. wide. £4,000

WASHSTANDS

Federal mahogany corner washstand on splay feet, 21½in. wide, circa 1800. £700

A marble-topped oak washstand, designed by A. W. N. Pugin, 108cm. width, circa 1850. £385

New England Federal mahogany washstand, circa 1800, 26½in. wide. £480

A George III mahogany toilet stand inlaid with satinwood bands and geometric boxwood lines, 24¼in. wide. £440

Victorian marble top oak washstand, 1860. £50

An early 19th century Dutch parquetry walnut bedside cupboard with galleried top, 19.5in. wide. £680

A Federal mahogany washstand, circa 1795, 39in. high, 23in. wide. £419

Victorian mahogany marble top washstand, 1860. £185

A George III Sheraton design mahogany serpentine front washstand, 17½in. wide. £340

WASHSTANDS

A semi-circular satinwood veneered bedside commode with yellow marble galleried top, 84cm. high. £550

A 20th century mahogany Sheraton-style dressing table/washstand with serpentine front, 49in. wide. £580

A George III mahogany wash basin stand with ring top, 2ft.7in. high. £390

Shaker pine, tiger maple and butternut washstand, 20¼in. wide. £6,993

A George III Sheraton design gentleman's washstand, 28in. wide. £850

A late Georgian mahogany washstand with gallery back, shelf and single drawer, 18in. wide. £100

A late George III inlaid mahogany corner washstand, 38½in. high, 22in. wide. £1,005

A mahogany washstand with small shelf, two drawers and pot shelf, 26 x 18 x 29in. high. £170

A late 18th century mahogany corner washstand with splay feet. £200

WASHSTANDS

A blue and white violin-shaped bidet, Qianlong, 61cm. long, on wood stand. £540

A mid 18th century Louis XV kingwood and tulip-wood heart-shaped toilet table, 2ft.6½in. high. £3,080

Victorian mahogany marble top washstand, 1860. £183

A Georgian style inlaid mahogany washstand with hinged top opening to reveal basin apertures, 1ft.8in. wide. £300

Victorian tiled back marble top washstand, 1860. £210

A Federal mahogany carved washstand, probably Mass., circa 1815, 20in. wide. £1,418

A George III mahogany pedestal washstand with hinged coffered folding top, 13in. wide. £800

A mahogany toilet pedestal with enclosed locker top and brass side carrying handles, 1ft.5in. wide. £170

Late 18th century mahogany bow fronted corner wash-stand on splay feet, 2ft.3½in. wide. £325

WASHSTANDS

A Georgian style part inlaid mahogany washstand, 1ft. 10in. wide. £150

Regency inlaid mahogany chest style commode. £225

A Georgian bow-front corner washstand with inlaid decoration, 2ft. wide. £260

Hepplewhite mahogany dressing stand, X stretchered, circa 1800. £410

Victorian mahogany and maple, tiled back, marble top washstand, 1865. £290

A Dutch marquetry and mahogany washstand with rouge royale marble inset top, 2ft.9in. wide, circa 1840. £1,000

A Classical Revival mahogany washstand, probably Boston, circa 1815, 17½in. diam. £10,312

A Regency period faded mahogany veneered toilet stand, 21in. wide. £200

A Regency oval two-tier washstand, the top tier with open centre, 24½in. wide. £770

WHATNOTS

One of a pair of George IV rosewood whatnots with bead-and-reel-moulded tops, 53½in. high.   **£5,500**

A snuff and gold lacquer etagere, the two shelves with pierced strapwork galleries, 28½in. long.   **£1,760**

Napoleon II ebonised and marquetry three-tier whatnot, 18¼in. wide.   **£290**

Regency rosewood whatnot, oblong, the three tiers with three-quarter spindle galleries, 1ft.2in. wide. **£820**

A George IV mahogany serving whatnot, the three-quarter galleried tiers joined by baluster supports, 40½in. wide.   **£880**

A Regency mahogany two-tier whatnot with easel top and ribbed supports, 21in. wide.   **£2,200**

A Regency brass three-tier whatnot with rosewood shelves, 15 x 28in. high.   **£2,900**

A gilt metal mounted mahogany etagere with two tiers crossbanded with satinwood and centred by a shell medallion, 23½in. wide. **£990**

Victorian figured walnut whatnot, three tier, on scroll feet, 2ft.5in. wide. **£340**

WHATNOTS

Victorian walnut four-tier whatnot, 1840. £385

A mid 19th century parquetry three tier etagere, 19½in. wide. £1,295

Victorian marble top whatnot, 1860. £295

An early 19th century three-tier mahogany whatnot, 45in. high. £280

An ebonised four-tier etagere with galleried top, circa 1830, 29in. wide, 49½in. high. £1,945

Victorian walnut whatnot, 1860. £185

One of a pair of Regency mahogany whatnots with vase finials, 17¾in. square. £1,945

A late Georgian bird's-eye maple four-tier etagere, 24in. wide, 31in. high. £2,915

An early 19th century mahogany whatnot, 1ft.6in. square. £450

WHATNOTS

A 19th century three-stage mahogany etagere, each shelf of oval form with pierced brass gallery. £400

A three-tier lacquered whatnot, 33 x 20in. £125

Victorian rosewood rectangular three-tier whatnot, stamped 'Charles & Edward', 19in. wide. £380

A George III mahogany whatnot, with deep spindled gallery above two shelves, circa 1805, 1ft. 7in. wide. £2,860

A Victorian ebonised and amboyna etagere, circa 1860, 2ft.4in. wide. £500

A Regency mahogany four-tier whatnot, circa 1810, 1ft.5in. wide. £770

A Victorian four-tier walnut whatnot with serpentine fronted display shelves, 3ft. 9in. high. £220

A Victorian mahogany corner whatnot with four graduated bow-front tiers, 80cm. wide. £550

A Victorian mahogany four-tier whatnot with tray top, 16½ x 10½ x 35in. high. £210

WINE COOLERS

A late Regency cellarette of Gothic style, 64in. wide. £1,835

A late Regency sarcophagus-shaped wine cooler, on hairy paw feet, 32in. wide. £880

A Victorian mahogany rectangular wine cooler with domed lid, 2ft.2in. wide. £150

A Regency period mahogany sarcophagus-shaped cellarette with original inset brass roller casters, 26in. high. £630

A George III mahogany campana-shaped wine cooler, 26in. diam. £5,200

A Regency small mahogany wine cooler with brass ring handles and paw feet, 16½in. high. £1,980

A Victorian mahogany sarcophagus-shaped wine cooler, minus lining, in the Chippendale-style, circa 1850, 29in. long. £550

Regency period sarcophagus-shaped mahogany cellarette, interior with twelve bottles and stoppers. £1,300

A late Regency mahogany sarcophagus wine cooler, 31in. wide. £770

WINE COOLERS

A Regency mahogany oval wine cooler in the manner of Gillows with lead-lined interior, 27¼in. wide.
£4,105

A Regency mahogany and inlaid cellarette of boat design, with triple hinged top, 1.02m. wide.
£4,600

A Regency mahogany wine cooler in the manner of Gillows, with oval tin liner, 29in. wide.
£4,320

A mid Georgian brass bound mahogany wine cooler with detachable tin liner, 23½in. wide.
£2,050

A George III mahogany wine cooler, the tapering brass bound body with carrying handles, 19½in. wide. £1,510

One of a pair of George III brass bound wine coolers with detachable tin liners, 27in. wide.
£5,400

A Federal inlaid mahogany wine cooler with lift top, 22in. wide.
£2,140

A late 18th century Sheraton style mahogany crossbanded and inlaid octagonal cellarette, 19in. wide.
£2,500

A George III brass bound mahogany wine cooler with arched brass carrying handle and lead lined interior, 13in. wide.
£7,150

WINE COOLERS

A late Regency mahogany sarcophagus-shaped wine cooler with lid enclosing a lead lined interior, 29½in. wide.   £1,320

A Regency mahogany wine cooler with lead-lined body, on ebonised claw feet, 28in. wide.   £3,455

A Regency mahogany sarco-phagus shaped wine cooler with lead lined interior, on paw feet, 29½in. wide.   £2,485

A George III mahogany brass bound wine cooler with carry-ing handles, 25in. wide. £2,265

One of two George III brass bound mahogany wine coolers with detachable liners, 25in. and 24in. wide.   £8,640

A Regency ormolu mounted mahogany wine cooler with hinged oval domed fan-shaped top, 29in. wide, 27in. high, 23in. deep.   £11,880

A large Regency mahogany and ebonised wine cooler in the manner of Gillows, with a lead-lined divided interior, 33in. wide.   £3,520

A George III mahogany oval wine cooler with line inlay, 24in.   £1,950

A late Georgian small maho-gany wine cellarette with brass ring handles, 20 x 19in.   £660

WINE COOLERS

A George III brass bound mahogany hexagonal cellarette, 28in. high, 17in. wide. £2,870

A Regency mahogany wine cooler with bronze lion-mask ring handles, on paw feet, 17in. wide. £715

A George III mahogany wine cooler with octagonal hinged lid enclosing a metal liner, 19½in. wide. £3,300

A William IV mahogany sarcophagus-shaped wine cooler with lead lined interior, 27½in. wide. £825

A George III mahogany wine cooler, the lined oval body banded in brass, 28in. wide. £2,800

A Regency mahogany and parcel gilt wine cooler with hinged lid enclosing a tin liner, 26¼in. wide. £1,540

A Federal inlaid walnut cellarette on stand, 1790-1810, 42½in. high, 18½in. wide. £1,705

A Regency mahogany wine cooler with lead lined interior, formerly with a lid, 39in. wide. £3,520

A Federal inlaid cherrywood cellarette and stand, 1790-1810, 36in. high. £4,965

INDEX